Symposium on

APPLICATIONS OF HOLOGRAPHY IN MECHANICS

AUGUST 23-25, 1971
UNIVERSITY OF SOUTHERN CALIFORNIA
LOS ANGELES, CALIFORNIA

Held as Part of
1971 WESTERN APPLIED MECHANICS CONFERENCE

Sponsored by
APPLIED MECHANICS DIVISION, ASME

Edited by
W. G. GOTTENBERG
UNIVERSITY OF COLORADO

THE AMERICAN SOCIETY OF MECHANICAL ENGINEERS
United Engineering Center • 345 East 47th Street • New York, N. Y. 10017

Library of Congress Catalog Card Number 78-172086

United Engineering Center
345 East 47th Street, New York, N.Y. 10017

Printed in USA

PREFACE

The advent of the laser as a coherent light source has permitted the development of holography as originally envisioned by Gabor in 1949 into a practical laboratory tool. This is borne out by the numerous technical applications of holography that have been reported since the mid-1960's. Included in these applications are holographic interferometry and the broad field of optical data processing which generally involves holography.

This symposium was organized for the purpose of bringing to the attention of workers in mechanics some recent developments in experimental mechanics which have been made possible by the development of holographic methods. Included are two papers which employ holographic interferometry to detect surface displacements of opaque bodies and to measure isopachics in transparent objects in a state of plane stress as an adjunct to photoelastic analysis. A survey of moiré methods is given in modern optical terms. Finally, the recently developed area of optical correlation is discussed in relation to the problem of measurement of surface strains.

We are indebted to the Western Committee of the Applied Mechanics Division of ASME for sponsoring the symposium. The cooperation of my co-authors, Professors Fourney and Sciammarella and Doctors Marom, Sawatari, and Mueller in preparing their papers for publication is gratefully acknowledged.

W. G. Gottenberg
August 1971

Contents

MEASUREMENT OF RIGID BODY MOTION BY HOLOGRAPHIC INTERFEROMETRY

W. G. Gottenberg
University of Colorado
Boulder, Colorado 80302

ABSTRACT

Holographic interferometry is briefly discussed with particular application to the measurement of the two step static displacement of the surface of a diffusely reflecting object. The analyses of fringe formation and localization that have been reported in the literature are reviewed. A geometric analysis of fringe formation is presented, reduced to the special case of plane rigid body motion, and interpreted in the light of using it for reduction of experimental fringe observations. An experiment is described for production of a holographic interferogram due to static plane motion of a diffusely reflecting surface. Experimental results from two such motions are analyzed and compared with the actual input conditions. A number of difficulties encountered in applying this experimental technique are discussed.

INTRODUCTION

One of the most technically interesting applications of holography is that of holographic interferometry. A number of modes of application of this type of interferometry are possible depending on the arrangement and sequence of use of the optical elements. In all cases it may be described as being two beam, common path interferometry.

One optical path is determined by the first exposure of the photographic plate to the usual object and reference waves to form a hologram. The second optical path is the same as the first with one exception. The exception may be that a mirror or scattering surface in either the path forming the object or reference wave is disturbed to a new static configuration to result in a phase difference between the first and second optical paths. The phase difference can also be obtained by altering the index of refraction of some portion of the medium through which the object or reference beams pass. The latter case is the holographic equivalent of a Mach-Zender interferometer used in wind tunnel studies. The former case with the displaced optical element being a diffusely reflecting surface is the one of interest in this paper.

Other options are provided by the manner in which the two beams are recorded in time. In the case of interest in this study, both legs of the interferometer which exist at two different instants of time are recorded as a double exposed hologram on the same photographic plate. Development of the plate and subsequent reconstruction as a hologram then yields two images of the interferometer -- one for each exposure. Since the hologram reproduces both the phase and amplitude of the wavefields from which it was formed; the reconstructed object waves, each due to one leg of the interferometer, will interfere in a meaningful way. That is, a fringe system will result which is governed by the effective optical path length differences in the two legs.

Another option for recording the two optical paths is to record the first leg holographically and then reconstruct it after exactly replacing the hologram. Now superposition or interference of the two paths occurs between the holographically reconstructed image of the first path which existed at some previous time and the interferometer path currently existing. This is referred to as real-time, holographic interferometry.

Two distinct advantages of double exposed interferometry over conventional interferometry for recording the motion of diffusely reflecting surfaces can now be stated. Firstly, since the two interferometer paths are common, the resulting fringe system is due only to motion of the scattering surface and is independent of the lack of smoothness of the surface -- apart from the fact that it be diffusely reflecting. The technique is truly differential and does not rely on the comparison of one optically smooth surface with another as in the case in conventional interferometry. Secondly, because the uniqueness of the scattering surface is recovered in the holographic image, the resulting fringe system can be related to the vector displacement of each surface point, not merely to that component coincident with the local normal to the surface as in conventional interferometry. This point will be amplified in the next section.

One observes two things when viewing the primary images reconstructed by a holographic interferogram. That portion of the interferometer which was recorded in the scene can be viewed at different perspectives as permitted by the dimensions of the hologram producing the well-known three dimensional effects of holography. Also as the line of sight is changed, the relative position of a particular fringe and some point on the surface of the scattering plate is seen to change. This indicates that the fringes are not in general localized on the surface of the object whose motion or surface deformation produced them.

A rigorous interpretation of the formation of fringes due to motion of a diffusely reflecting surface as in the two step, double exposed, static case discussed above involves accounting for the combination of the two reflected wavefields. It is the average of their intensities in time which was recorded on the photographic plate and which produced the fringe system. The fringe order associated with a given line of sight intersecting a given point on the surface of the diffuse reflecter is due to interference of the two fields scattered by the entire surface being examined.

The analysis of this problem was first undertaken by Hanes and Hildebrand (1) who concluded that motion of the scattering surface in all of its six degrees of freedom could be computed by knowing the fringe order at a particular point on the surface along three lines of sight intersecting the point as well as by knowing the position of fringe localization along each of those lines. This poses a difficult experimental task. More recently Stetson (2,3) and Walles (4) have performed similar more rigorous analyses of this general problem of fringe visibility and localization. Additionally, Molin and Stetson (5,6) and Walles (4) performed experiments to verify the spacing and localization of fringes predicted by these analyses for simple rigid motions of diffusely reflecting surfaces.

An apparent simplification of the experimental problem of relating fringe spacing and localization to the motion of a surface was suggested in a paper by Aleksandrov and Bonch-Bruevich (7). They contended that if a point on the object and the fringe system at that point along a particular line of sight were viewed with an instrument of sufficient depth of field to focus simultaneously the fringes and the object surface that measurement of the fringe order at that point obtained for three different lines of sight would permit determination of the displacement vector at that point. A more detailed explanation of this same principle was given in a later paper by Sollid (8).

Both of these authors analysed the fringe formation problem by a geometrical approach which ignored contributions to the phase difference in the two interfering fields at a point on the object from those portions of the fields outside the neighborhood of the point. A theoretical justification for this approach was provided later by both Stetson (3) and Walles (4).

This simplified treatment of the relation of fringe shape and spacing to the deformation of a diffuse reflector has formed the basis of a number of recently published papers. In all cases the approach has been to provide a known two step, static deformation or rigid body motion of the reflecting surface in terms of magnitude or direction or both and then to verify that the fringe system is in agreement with that predicted by the geometrical theory. Biaxial, in-plane extensions of a plane membrane surface were studied by Ennos (9) and Wilson (10). Simple rigid body translations and rotations of a plane surface were treated by Viénot et.al. (11) and Molin and Stetson (5,6). Wilson (12) examined the fringe system due to rigid rotation and twisting of a circular shaft about its axis.

The aim of the present paper is related but somewhat different. Two step, static, rigid body motions of a plane diffusely reflecting surface are studied. Moreover, the experiment is contrived so that the displacement vector of a generic point on the object's surface is of known magnitude and lies in a known plane perpendicular to the surface. However, the analysis of the resulting fringe system to calculate the displacement vector only assumes a priori that plane motion occurred. The direction of the displacement vector in the plane and its magnitude are then computed from the fringe position measurements and compared with the known input. The analytical and experimental techniques developed provide the first step toward solution of the more difficult problem of ascertaining general rigid body motion or general surface deformation from fringe position analysis.

In the sections to follow the geometric analysis of fringe formation is briefly summarized and reduced to the special plane motion case. Some interesting observations about anticipated experimental difficulties are made from the analytical results. The experiment is next described and finally analytical-experimental results are presented.

ANALYSIS

Following Sollid (8), the geometric analysis for fringe formation due to static object motion for double exposed holographic interferometry will be developed. Reduction of these results to the special case of plane motion will follow.

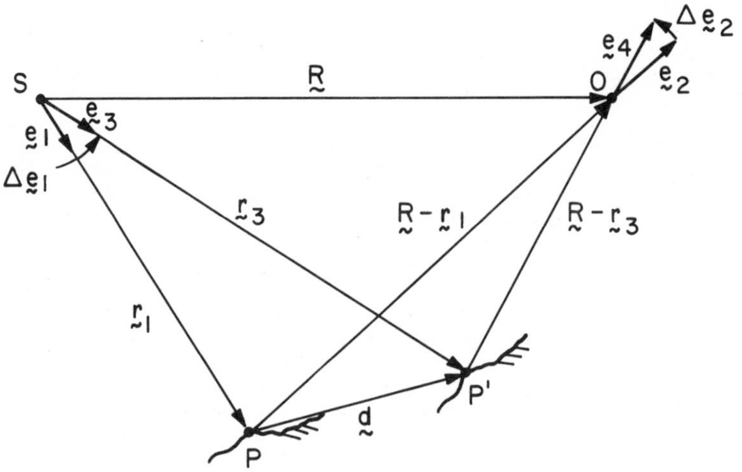

Figure 1. Ray Geometry for Fringe Formation

S is the point light source

O is the arbitrary observation point

P, P' are two positions of the same generic surface point

$\underset{\sim}{d}$ is the displacement vector

With reference to Figure 1 consider two generic surface points P and P' referring to the same point on the object in two states of deformation. These two points are in reality associated with points on the holographically reconstructed images of the object recorded at two past instants of time. A point source of coherent light existed at point S at each of these instants of time. The current location of an observer is at point O. The position vector of P' relative to P is $\underset{\sim}{d}$. In all that follows $\underset{\sim}{d}$ will be assumed to be directed as shown but it might as well be directed to P and the analysis will not make the distinction. In other words the analysis will only determine the direction of $\underset{\sim}{d}$ to within the angle π.

To compute the path length difference between the two configurations we note that the length of the path SPO is

$$\Delta_1 = \underset{\sim}{e}_1 \cdot \underset{\sim}{r}_1 + \underset{\sim}{e}_2 \cdot (\underset{\sim}{R} - \underset{\sim}{r}_1)$$

and the length of the path SP'O is

$$\Delta_2 = \underset{\sim}{e}_3 \cdot \underset{\sim}{r}_3 + \underset{\sim}{e}_4 \cdot (\underset{\sim}{R} - \underset{\sim}{r}_3)$$, where $\underset{\sim}{e}_1, \underset{\sim}{e}_2, \underset{\sim}{e}_3, \underset{\sim}{e}_4$ are unit vectors.

Express $\underset{\sim}{e}_3$ and $\underset{\sim}{e}_4$ as

$$\underset{\sim}{e}_3 = \underset{\sim}{e}_1 + \Delta\underset{\sim}{e}_1$$

and $$\underset{\sim}{e}_4 = \underset{\sim}{e}_2 + \Delta\underset{\sim}{e}_2 .$$

Finally, the path length difference is

$$\Delta = \Delta_2 - \Delta_1$$
$$= \underset{\sim}{e}_1 \cdot \underset{\sim}{r}_3 + \Delta\underset{\sim}{e}_1 \cdot \underset{\sim}{r}_3 + \underset{\sim}{e}_2 \cdot (\underset{\sim}{R} - \underset{\sim}{r}_3)$$
$$+ \Delta\underset{\sim}{e}_2 \cdot (\underset{\sim}{R} - \underset{\sim}{r}_2) - \underset{\sim}{e}_1 \cdot \underset{\sim}{r}_1 - \underset{\sim}{e}_2 \cdot (\underset{\sim}{R} - \underset{\sim}{r}_1)$$
$$= (\underset{\sim}{e}_2 - \underset{\sim}{e}_1) \cdot (\underset{\sim}{r}_1 - \underset{\sim}{r}_3) + \Delta\underset{\sim}{e}_1 \cdot \underset{\sim}{r}_3 + \Delta\underset{\sim}{e}_2 \cdot (\underset{\sim}{R} - \underset{\sim}{r}_3) .$$

If we assume that the motion of the object is small compared with the distance from the source to the object, i.e.,

$$|\underset{\sim}{r}_1| \simeq |\underset{\sim}{r}_3| >> |\underset{\sim}{d}| = |\underset{\sim}{r}_3 - \underset{\sim}{r}_1| ,$$

so that, $\Delta\underset{\sim}{e}_1$ is nearly perpendicular to $\underset{\sim}{r}_3$ and $\Delta\underset{\sim}{e}_2$ is nearly perpendicular to $(\underset{\sim}{R} - \underset{\sim}{r}_3)$, then we get

$$\Delta = (\underset{\sim}{e}_2 - \underset{\sim}{e}_1) \cdot (\underset{\sim}{r}_1 - \underset{\sim}{r}_3) .$$

But $\underset{\sim}{r}_1 - \underset{\sim}{r}_3 = -\underset{\sim}{d}$, so that

$$\Delta = (\underset{\sim}{e}_1 - \underset{\sim}{e}_2) \cdot \underset{\sim}{d} . \qquad (1)$$

Now it becomes necessary to interpret equation 1 in terms of specific geometry. For simplicity assume that the source provides plane wave illumination, implying that

$$\underset{\sim}{e}_1 = \underset{\sim}{e}_2$$

and that the object is viewed through an instrument focused at infinity so that

$$\underset{\sim}{e}_2 = \underset{\sim}{e}_4 .$$

A reference frame is established relative to the local surface normal at P and we consider $\underset{\sim}{d}$ to be a plane vector. Thus without loss of generality we take $\underset{\sim}{e}_1$, $\underset{\sim}{e}_2$, and $\underset{\sim}{d}$ to be coplanar. The input angle ϕ, the output or viewing angle γ, and the direction of displacement β are defined in Figure 2. Note that rotation of the surface about an axis perpendicular to the plane of $\underset{\sim}{e}_1$, $\underset{\sim}{e}_2$, and $\underset{\sim}{d}$ can be determined by comparing the plane displacement vectors associated with two or more points on the surface. Continuity of the surface is preserved during deformation.

With reference to equation 1 we now have

$$\underset{\sim}{e}_1 \cdot \underset{\sim}{d} = d \cos(\beta+\phi)$$

and

$$\underset{\sim}{e}_2 \cdot \underset{\sim}{d} = d \cos(\gamma-\beta)$$

$$= d\cos(\beta-\gamma),$$

where $d = |\tilde{d}|$.

Thus

$$\Delta = d[\cos(\beta+\phi) + \cos(\beta-\gamma)] . \qquad (2)$$

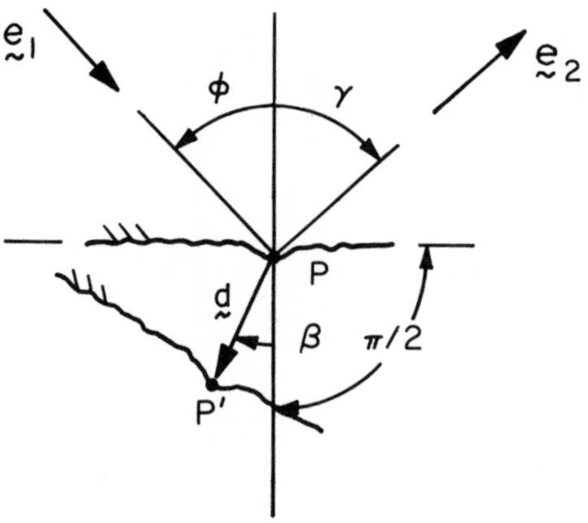

Figure 2. Ray Geometry Relative to Local Surface Normal

Consider that distortions of the object do not change its surface reflectivity so that the total change in the effective optical path length is due only to changes in geometry. On that basis we can state that the condition for formation of dark fringes at O will be given by

$$\Delta = \frac{\lambda}{2}, \frac{3\lambda}{2}, \ldots$$

$$= \left(\frac{2n-1}{2}\right)\lambda; \quad n = 1,2, \ldots \qquad (3)$$

where λ is the wavelength of the coherent illumination. Also for convenience let

$$|\tilde{d}| = m\lambda$$

where m is clearly a positive number. Then the condition for dark fringe formation (equation 3 along with equation 2) becomes

$$\frac{n-1/2}{m} = \cos(\beta-\gamma) + \cos(\beta+\phi) . \qquad (4)$$

For a given displacement condition, i.e., given m and β and for a given input beam direction (ϕ) we interpret equation 4 as relating the order of the dark fringe seen at P to the direction of the line of sight given by γ. To gain a better insight into the significance of this equation in the interpretation of experimental data, the left hand side of the equation (the fringe function) has been plotted as a function of viewing angle.

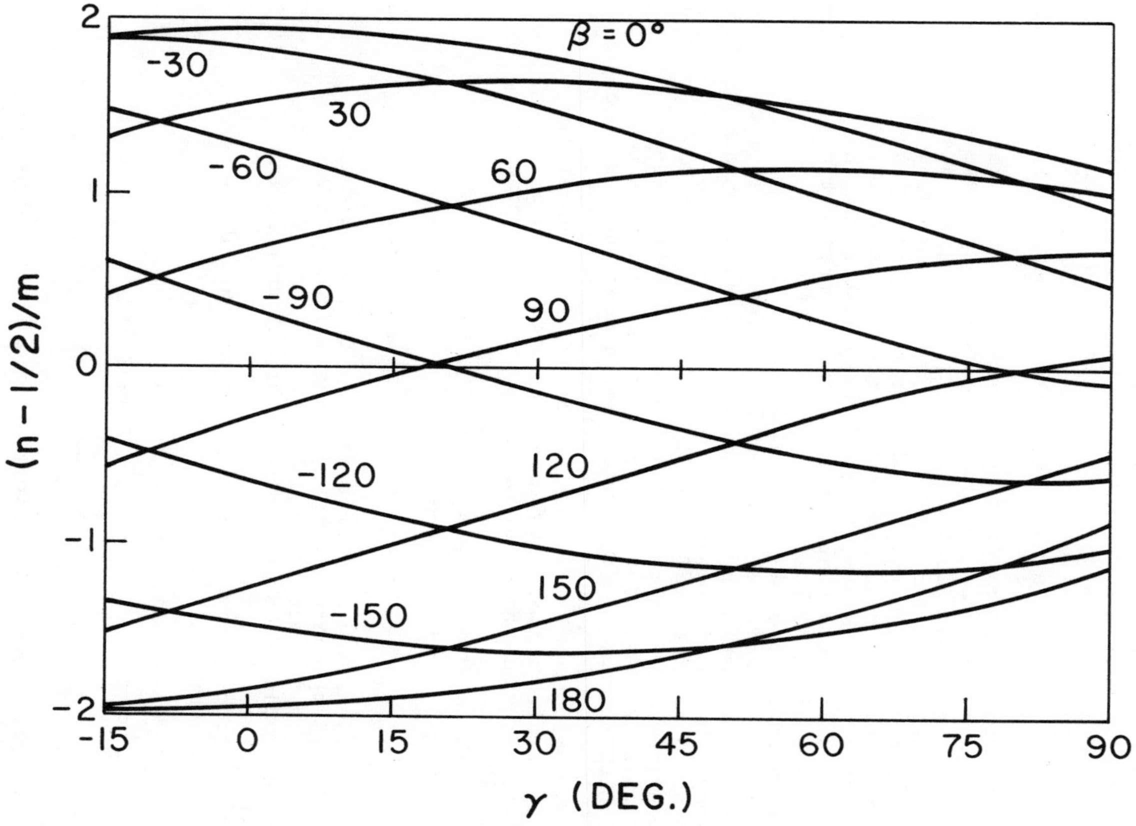

Figure 3. Variation of Fringe Function with Direction of Viewing, (ϕ = 20 deg.).

These results are shown in Figure 3 with the direction of the displacement vector (β) as a parameter for a particular input beam direction (ϕ = 20 deg.). The maximum practical range of γ is shown, namely, the obtuse angle between the input beam and the front or illuminated side of the object.

These curves indicate the effective sensitivity of the experiment in the sense of showing the variation of fringe order with viewing angle for given m, β, and ϕ. Note in particular for a mean line of sight coincident with the direction of the displacement vector ($\gamma = \beta \pm \pi$) that small variations in direction of the line of sight produce only slight changes in the fringe order. However, the curves have a maximum slope for γ and β differing by $\pi/2$ indicating a maximum sensitivity to variations in γ.

Note also that the curvatures of the curves (except for sign) are defined uniquely by the direction of the displacement vector to within $\pm\pi$. That is, the change of the fringe function with γ for a particular β (say -150 deg.) is the same except for sign as it is for $\beta + \pi$ (30 deg.). This point will be brought out again later when the data reduction procedure is described. It is an expected result since it was tacitly assumed at the beginning of this analysis that the sequence of constructing the two holograms could be read from the reconstruction. Obviously, such information is not available.

Next consider equation 4 in the light of using it to find m and β from experimental results. For a given experimental arrangement ϕ is known and variations of the line of sight (γ) are made so as to align dark fringes (n = 1,2, ...) over the point of observation (P) on the surface of the object. Hence each experimentally determined pair of γ and n generate a new equation 4 in the unknowns m and β. It would seem that two such equations would provide a consistent system for their determination. However, the absolute fringe order is not generally known nor is the direction of numbering for increasing or decreasing fringe order number known. Thus we really have four unknown quantities.

With each value of viewing angle in the sequence γ_i, i = 1,2, ... associated with a dark fringe we write

$$n = k \pm n_i, \qquad \text{where k and } n_i \text{ are integers.}$$

For $n_i = 3$, for example, the fringe order n is k ± 3 and the sign is determined by whether or not the next fringe to a particular side was numbered correctly, i.e., either 3 + 1 or 3 - 1. Note n_i could be associated with bright fringes and then n_i would range ±1/2, ±3/2, ...

Rewrite equation 4 with this notation and expand the right hand side,

$$\frac{k \pm n_i - 1/2}{m} = \cos\beta \cos\phi - \sin\beta \sin\phi + \cos\beta \cos\gamma_i + \sin\beta \sin\gamma_i \; . \qquad (5)$$

Note the first two terms of the right hand side are independent of γ_i. Write a similar equation for the $(i + \ell)^{\underline{th}}$ fringe order and subtract the two equations to get

$$\frac{\pm n_i \mp n_{i+\ell}}{m} = \cos\beta \, (\cos\gamma_i - \cos\gamma_{i+\ell}) + \sin\beta \, (\sin\gamma_i - \sin\gamma_{i+\ell}) \; . \qquad (6)$$

We may write a similar result by subtracting the $(i + \ell)^{\underline{th}}$ from the $(i + \ell + k)^{\underline{th}}$ equation. Solving this result along with equation 6 for m, equating, dividing both sides by $\cos\beta$, and ignoring the redundancy in sign gives finally,

$$\tan\beta = [n_i(\cos\gamma_{i+\ell} - \cos\gamma_{i+\ell+k}) + n_{i+\ell}(\cos\gamma_{i+\ell+k} - \cos\gamma_i)$$
$$+ n_{i+\ell+k}(\cos\gamma_i - \cos\gamma_{i+\ell})] \; / \; [n_i(\sin\gamma_{i+\ell}$$
$$- \sin\gamma_{i+\ell+k}) + n_{i+\ell}(\sin\gamma_{i+\ell+k} - \sin\gamma_i)$$
$$+ n_{i+\ell+k}(\sin\gamma_i - \sin\gamma_{i+\ell})] \; . \qquad (7)$$

Several points should be made about this result. First, note the indetermenancy of β to within $\pm\pi$ as was seen earlier. Second, the only restriction on the experimental assignment of fringes orders is that they be consistently numbered. Hence if $n_i = 3$, then $n_{i+\ell} = \{ \begin{smallmatrix} 3 \; 1/2 \\ 2 \; 1/2 \end{smallmatrix}$ must correspond to the next bright fringe resulting from a change in γ. By the same token, $n_{i+\ell+k} = \{ \begin{smallmatrix} 4 \text{ or } 4 \; 1/2 \\ 2 \text{ or } 2 \; 1/2 \end{smallmatrix}$, etc. Finally note that this result points out a basic experimental difficulty. To illustrate let $n_i = 1$, $n_{i+\ell} = 2$, and $n_{i+\ell+k} = 3$, then $\gamma_i = \gamma_1$, $\gamma_{i+\ell} = \gamma_2$, $\gamma_{i+\ell+k} = \gamma_3$ and

$$\tan\beta = \frac{\cos\gamma_1 - 2\cos\gamma_2 + \cos\gamma_3}{\sin\gamma_1 - 2\sin\gamma_2 + \sin\gamma_3} \; .$$

If it happens that γ_1, γ_2, γ_3 are nearly the same or are associated with a nearly straight line portion of Figure 3 for a particular β then,

$$\cos\gamma_2 \simeq \frac{\cos\gamma_1 + \cos\gamma_3}{2}$$

and

$$\sin\gamma_2 \simeq \frac{\sin\gamma_1 + \sin\gamma_3}{2} \; .$$

Substitution of these expressions leads to an indeterminant value of $\tan\beta$. Thus the region of viewing angles providing the best sensitivity in the fringe function yields poor accuracy in the determination of β, the first step in the data reduction procedure. Clearly the best results will be obtained for γ_i, $\gamma_{i+\ell}$, $\gamma_{i+\ell+k}$ covering the widest range possible. This is illustrated in the section on experimental results.

Knowing β we return to equation 6 from which we solve m. Choose the upper or lower set of signs as needed to make m positive (recall that $m\lambda$ was the magnitude of the displacement vector). Now in equation 5 we know β and m as well as the correct sign on n_i so solve it for k. Since k must be an integer round off the value of k determined from equation 5 to its nearest integer value and substitute this in equation 5 to solve for the correct value of m.

A digital computer program was written to perform these calculations using all equally spaced combinations of n_i taken 3 at a time.

EXPERIMENT

The essential features of the experimental apparatus are

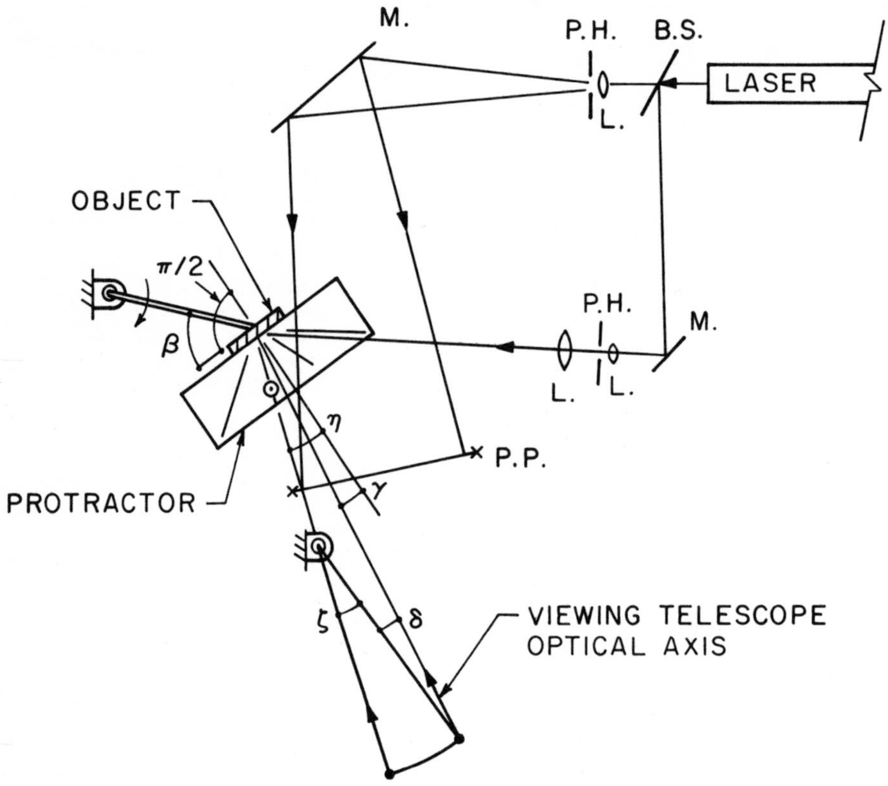

Figure 4. Schematic View of the Experimental Arrangement. (The elements labeled L are lenses, those marked M are mirrors, P.H. stands for pinholes, P.P. is the photographic plate, and B.S. is the beam splitter)

shown in Figure 4. The light source was a 15 mw. He-Ne continuous wave laser. A beam splitter directed about 15% of the intensity of the laser beam to the reference beam which was made spherically divergent by passing it through a lens and spatial filter. A plane object wave was obtained by means of a lens, pinhole, and telescope arrangement. The photographic emulsion was Kodak 649F on a 4 x 5 in. glass plate.

The diffusely reflecting object was an aluminum plate about 1 1/2 in. square whose surface was etched with nitric acid and then ruled by pen with a 1/2 in. spaced grid. The object was fixed with its front surface in a vertical plane to the free end of an arm which could be rotated by known angles in a horizontal plane. In addition, the object could be rotated to any desired fixed position relative to the arm about a vertical axis passing through its front surface. Since the rotation of the arm was small (100 - 200 μrad.) compared with the desired resolution of β and since the arm was relatively long (5.33 in.) all points on the surface of the object experienced virtually the same plane motion in a horizontal plane. In case the face of the object was perpendicular to the arm (β = 90 deg.), the magnitudes of displacement of all points on the surface of the object were the same and in the plane of the surface. At the other extreme, with the object surface in line with the arm (β = 0 deg.), the displacements of all points were virtually normal to the object surface and proportional in magnitude to their respective horizontal distances from the axis of rotation of the arm.

Rotation of the arm in a horizontal plane was obtained by supporting the arm on a torsional elastic pivot (torsional stiffness 212 in. lb/rad) and then applying a moment by extending two soft (0.2 lb/in.) helical springs attached to opposing lever arms fastened to the arm at its axis of rotation. Extension of the springs was effected by means of calibrated micrometer screws which were adjusted between exposures. Resolution of the rotation imposed was about 1 μrad. and the rotation could be established to an accuracy of about 3 μrad. The fact that rotation of the arm did indeed occur in a horizontal plane was verified in all cases by noting that the fringes were parallel to a vertical center line on the object surface and equally spaced when viewed from infinity.

Establishment of input beam and viewing angles relative to the object surface was accomplished by means of a horizontal protractor plate aligned just in front of, but not touching the object surface. Radial lines at a number of angular positions were milled into the surface of the plate. A small cylindrical rod whose ends were turned to a point was positioned vertically over a radial slot on the protractor by sliding it down a close-fitting hole in a cylindrical button one end of which rested on the protractor. By this means the upper visible pointed end of the rod was made to correspond to a particular radial line to within 0.1 deg. Alignment of the input plane wave beam was accomplished by causing the shadow of the pointed rod to coincide with the vertical center line on the front face of the object. Another similarly located rod was used to obtain initial alignment of the fringe viewing apparatus.

Several methods of viewing and analyzing the fringes in the holographic images were evaluated. For example, in one case the hologram was reconstructed by a converging spherical reference beam so that projected real images of the primary images could be studied. The line of sight was established by the position on the photographic plate through which the reference beam was projected and the fringe system was scanned in space by a traveling microdensitometer. It was found that this scheme and several others which involved trying to realign the hologram to the reference beam were impractical without using elaborate relocating fixtures. All angles in the hologram reconstruction must be preserved with essentially no error.

The only practical solution was found to be to veiw the primary images as virtual images superimposed on the object. All optical elements were left untouched after constructing the hologram (including the beam splitter) and the hologram was replaced in a kinematic mount correct to within a few fringes. In order to avoid confusion between the holographically reconstructed images of the object and the object itself, the object beam was blocked.

The reconstructed fringes and object were viewed by means of a telescope whose effective aperture was 25 mm and whose objective lens was about 48 in. from the object. Use of this instrument ensured that the fringes and the area of the object under examination were simultaneously in focus. Also the solid angle subtended at the telescope aperture was within the restrictions placed by the analysis of Stetson (2) and Walles (4) on the use of the geometric interpretation of fringe formation.

The telescope was attached to an end of an arm, the other end of which was fixed to a bearing so that the arm could move in a horizontal plane. In addition, the telescope could rotate about a vertical axis which intersected its optical axis. These rotations were measured as the angles labeled ζ and δ respectively in Figure 4.

Initial alignment of this instrument involved orienting it such that the crosshair in the telescope eyepiece, the axis of rotation of the telescope arm, a pointer on the protractor plate at a known angle η, and the vertical centerline of the object were all coincident. With this arrangement the viewing angle mentioned in the geometric fringe analysis could be calculated by the equation

$$\gamma = \eta - (\zeta - \delta) \tag{7}$$

Experimental error in the determination of the angle γ was found to be less than ±0.1 deg. by measuring the known angle between two marker pins on the protractor plate.

The experiment was performed by constructing a holographic interferogram, aligning the viewing telescope as described above, and then adjusting the angles ζ and δ to bring the sequence of fringes of order n_i in alignment with the telescope crosshair and the point on the object being studied, e.g., the vertical centerline. The sequence of angles γ_i was then computed from equation 7. Having the actual object superimposed on the holographic images was of considerable help in performing these measurements since the point on the object being studied could always be located readily by returning to ambient room light.

A distinct advantage of this experiment over others described in the literature is that one only measures angles -- distance measurements are unnecessary.

EXPERIMENTAL RESULTS

Double exposed holograms were constructed for plane rigid body motion of a diffusely reflecting surface in the manner described above for two cases: displacement normal to the plane (β = 0) and in-plane displacement (β = 90 deg). In the first case the observation angle (γ) ranged from about 5 deg. to 40 deg. and in the second case from about 10 deg. to 30 deg. With reference to Figure 3 it can be seen that data were obtained on about the most curved portion of the fringe function vs. γ curve for β = 0 and along the most nearly straight portion of the curve for $\beta=\pi/2$. In both instances the variation in fringe order with viewing angle was studied at three locations along a horizontal line on the object surface: at the vertical centerline and at the points 1/2 in. to either side of the centerline. In both cases studied, the arm to which the object was attached was rotated 174 μrad. which meant that about 11 consecutive dark fringes could be identified over the ranges of viewing angles specified for each case.

It was of interest to determine the accuracy with which the displacement vector at a point on the surface could be computed from the experimental data. Since a single computation only involved data associated with 3 fringes and since measurements were made at typically 11 integer order fringes as well as all intermediate 1/2 order fringes (the bright fringes) there was a redundant amount of data. To make the utmost use of those data calculations of β, m, and k were made for all combinations of fringes taken 3 at a time and separated by the same number starting at a fringe spacing of 1 and progressing to a spacing of 5.

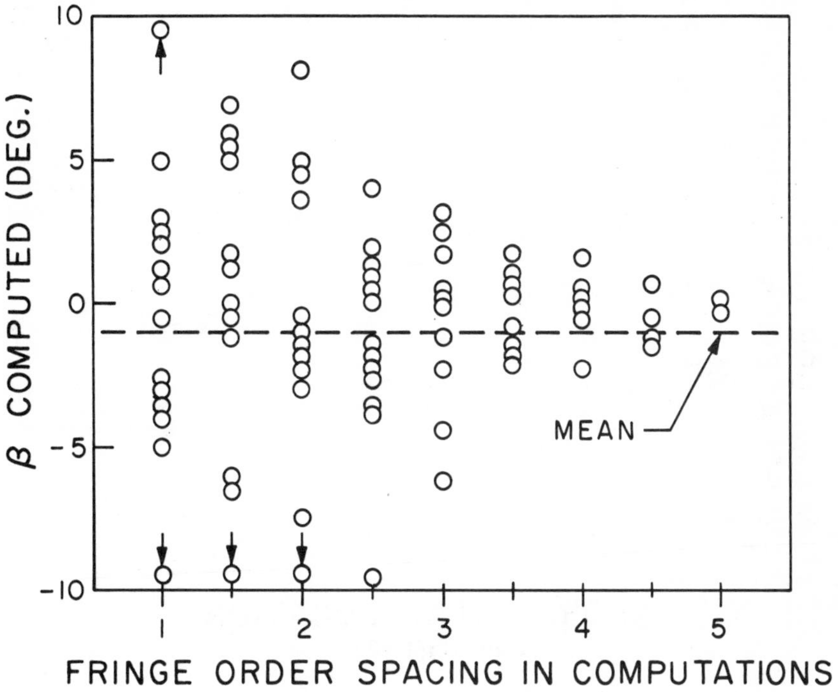

Figure 5. Distribution of Computed Values of β Depending on the Fringe Order Spacing in the Computations.

Typical results are shown in Figure 5 for the calculation of β for an input β = 0. As was expected the accuracy of the calculation improved as the fringe spacing increased. The mean value shown (0.4 deg.) is based on the results of all calculations and did not change significantly as the fringe order spacing increased. Also the calculated values shown were found to be distributed about the mean in a nearly Gaussian manner. The standard deviation and the ±95% confidence limits were calculated routinely.

Figure 6 shows the mean calculated values of m and β (and k) at the three horizontal locations. The error bars indicate the ±95% confidence limits of the calculated results. The calculated direction of the displacement vector is correct to within about 1/2 deg. and its magnitude is not significantly different from the input. Another experiment for β = 0 in which the magnitude of displacement was about 1/2 of that for the results shown led to the same conclusions.

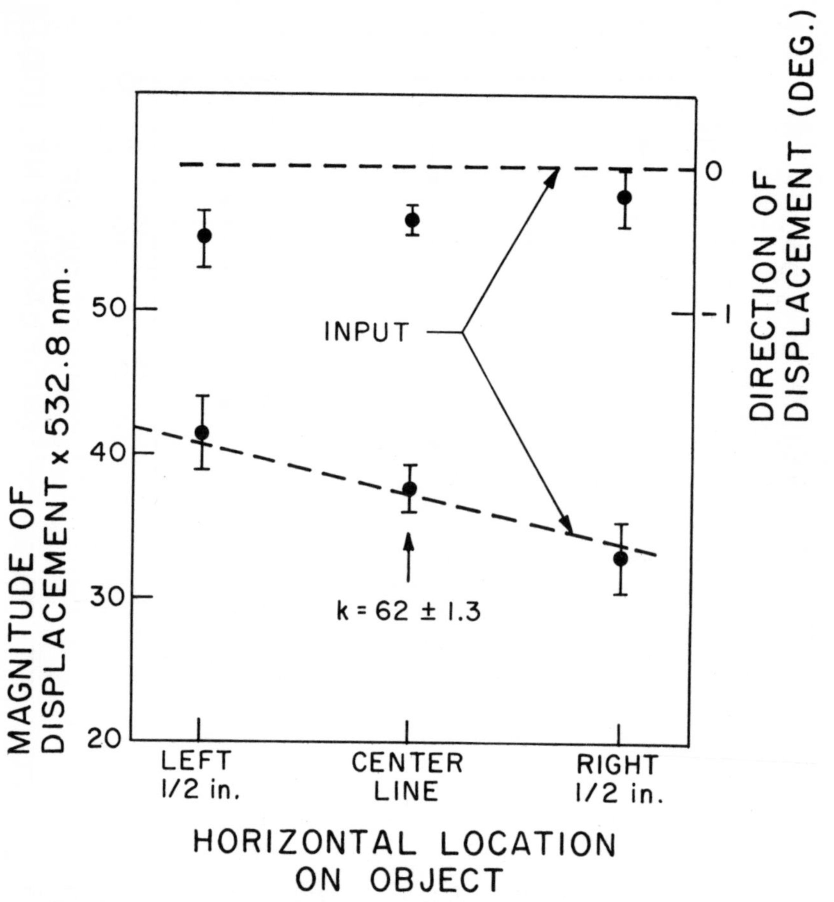

Figure 6. Computed Results and Experimental Input for β and m at Three Horizontal Locations.

The computed results from the experiment for β = 90 deg. are shown in Figure 7. Note that the magnitude of the displacement vector at the three points examined agrees very well with the input, but that the direction is in error by about 5 deg. It was expected from the above analytical considerations that the β = 90 deg. case would lead to larger errors in the calculated results because of the difficulty in computing tanβ in a region where the fringe function varied nearly linearly with viewing angle.

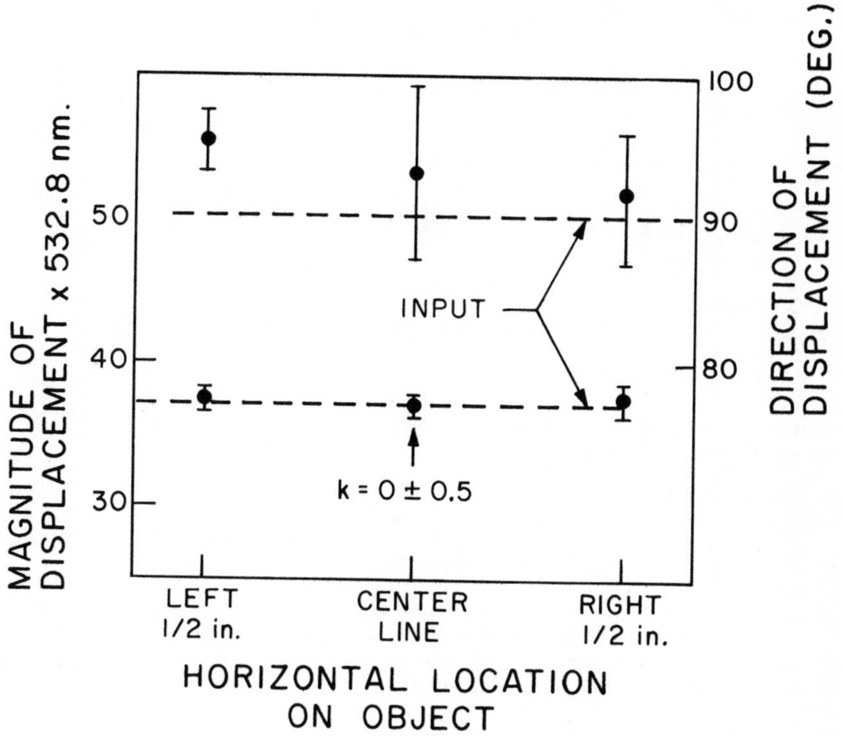

Figure 7. Computed Results and Experimental Input for β and m at Three Horizontal Locations.

CONCLUSIONS

The results presented verify that the geometric analysis of fringe formation for the rigid motion of a diffusely reflecting surface is correct if the appropriate experimental precautions are taken. Experimental techniques have been developed for measuring a plane displacement vector at any point on the displaced surface (or the components of a more general displacement vector in a particular plane). Typical experimental results have been obtained which illustrate difficulties in application of this technique.

Extension of the method to measurement of the general motion of diffuse surfaces is obvious and straightforward.

ACKNOWLEDGEMENTS

The support of this project by the National Science Foundation through a grant to the University of Colorado is gratefully acknowledged.

REFERENCES

1. Haines, K. A. and Hildebrand, B. P., "Interferometric Measurements on Diffuse Surfaces by Holographic Techniques," IEEE Trans. on Instrumentation and Measurement, Vol. IM-15, No. 4, Dec. 1966, pp. 149-161.

2. Stetson, K. A., "A Rigorous Treatment of the Fringes of Hologram Interferometry," OPTIK, Vol. 29, No. 4, 1969, pp. 386-400.

3. Stetson, K. A., "The Argument of the Fringe Function in Hologram Interferometry of General Deformations," OPTIK, Vol. 31, No. 6, 1970, pp. 576-591.

4. Walles, S., "Visibility and Localization of Fringes in Holographic Interferometry of Diffusely Reflecting Surfaces," Arkiv för Fysik, Vol. 40, No. 26, 1969, pp. 299-403.

5. Molin, N. and Stetson, K. A., "Measurement of Fringe Loci and Localization in Hologram Interferometry for Pivot Motion, In-Plane Rotation and In-Plane Translation, Part I," OPTIK, Vol. 31, No. 2, 1970, pp. 157-177.

6. Molin, N. and Stetson, K. A., "Measurement of Fringe Loci and Localization in Hologram Interferometry for Pivot Motion, In-Plane Rotation and In-Plane Translation, Part II," OPTIK, Vol. 31, No. 3, 1970, pp. 281-291.

7. Aleksandrov, E. B. and Bonch-Bruevich, A. M., "Investigation of Surface Strains by the Hologram Technique," Soviet Physics-Technical Physics, Vol. 12, No. 2, Aug. 1967, pp. 258-265.

8. Sollid, J. E., "Holographic Interferometry Applied to Measurements of Small Static Displacements of Diffusely Reflecting Surfaces," Applied Optics, Vol. 8, No. 8, Aug. 1 1969, pp. 1587-1595.

9. Ennos, A. E., "Measurement of In-Plane Surface Strain by Hologram Interferometry," J. of Scientific Instruments, Vol. 1, 1968, pp. 731-734.

10. Wilson, A. D., "In-Plane Displacement of a Stressed Membrane with a Hole Measured by Holographic Interferometry," Applied Optics, Vol. 10, No. 4, Apr. 1971, pp. 908-912.

11. Viénot, J. Ch., Froehly, C. L., Monneret, J., and Pasteur, J., "Hologram Interferometry: Surface Displacement Fringe Analysis as an Approach to the Study of Mechanical Strains and Other Applications to the Determination of Anisotropy in Transparent Objects," The Engineering Uses of Holography, Cambridge University Press, 1970, pp. 133-150.

12. Wilson, A. D., "Holographically Observed Torsion in a Cylindrical Shaft," Applied Optics, Vol. 9, No. 9, Sept. 1970, pp. 2093-2097.

ADVANCES IN HOLOGRAPHIC PHOTOELASTICITY

M. E. Fourney
Department of Aeronautics and Astronautics
University of Washington

ABSTRACT

The application of holographic interferometry to photoelasticity is discussed. An analysis of the method is presented and the importance of the complex amplitude of the wavefront emphasized. The relationships between the isochromatic and isopachic fringes in the combined fringe pattern are discussed and several methods of separating these fringe families are presented. A method for recording and reconstructing the polarization of a wavefront is reviewed and it is shown that the entire family of isoclinics may be obtained from a single test. Extensions of the holographic photoelasticity method, which include dynamic problems, are illustrated. Some current three-dimensional techniques are reviewed and a new method is proposed.

INTRODUCTION

Photoelasticity has been an important method of experimental stress analysis for the last half century. It has primarily been limited to the determination of the difference in the principal stress components and their directions. This is accomplished by measuring the relative retardation of two orthogonal polarization states of a light ray propagating through a two-dimensional model. The directions are determined separately by measuring the orientation of the principal optical axes at each point in the model. Many methods have been devised to determine the individual stress components; one of the more important of these is the use of interferometry to measure the absolute retardation.

The interferometric photoelastic method was introduced in 1929 by Favre[1] as a point by point method. It was later extended to a full-field representation by Post[2] and Nisida and Saito[3]. Although the potential of this method has been recognized for some time, it has been infrequently used. This was due primarily to the stringent requirements on the quality of the optical elements and the close tolerance on positioning of these elements. Holographic interferometry and advances in laser technology have relaxed to a great extent these restrictions and permit greater utilization of the interferometry method in photoelasticity. The application of holographic interferometry was suggested by Fourney[4] and Hovanesion, Brcic, and Powell[5]. Since then, a considerable interest has developed in the method and numerous papers have resulted. Included among these was a more detailed analysis of the method by Fourney and Mate[6], Hosp and Wutze[7], and Holloway[8]. One desirable aspect of the method is that it is directly applicable to dynamic problems as demonstrated by Holloway[8].

The interferometric method, either classical or holographic, results in a fringe pattern that is a combination of both the isochromatics and isopachics, i.e., the sum and difference of the principal stresses. Although on one hand this is the desirable feature of the method in that it allows the individual principal stress components to be determined from a single test, it also results in some difficulties with interpretation. This interpretation problem results in a cross modulation of the two fringe families and has been the subject of several studies[8,9,10]. The salient feature of all of these studies is that, under certain conditions, a straightforward interpretation of the combined pattern is not possible. As a result, several methods for the separation of the two families of fringes has been made. Dudderar and O'Regan[10] have demonstrated a technique for the separation of the fringes which is applicable to both static and dynamic problems.

The major distinguishing feature in the application of holography to photoelasticity is the importance of the polarization state of the wavefront to be recorded. In many applications, this contains as much information as the wavefront phase change. The analysis presented here accounts for this using a complex amplitude for the light wave rather than the scalar representation normally used in holography.

ANALYSIS OF HOLOGRAPHIC INTERFEROMETRY

Holographic interferometry is used to analyze the photoelastic model. Interference is obtained between the wavefronts that propagate through the model in two different loading states. The major difference between holographic interferometry and conventional interferometry is that in holography the wavefronts that are compared were originally separated in time; whereas, in conventional interferometry they have been spatially separated. The wavefront is stored in the hologram and can be reconstructed at a later time. Two methods will be discussed; the double exposure method in which wavefronts which exist at two different times are stored in the hologram and reconstructed at a later time simultaneously. The second method is the real-time method. A wavefront is stored in the hologram which is then processed, and that wavefront is reconstructed and compared to a wavefront that exists at that instant.

The basic arrangements used in the two-step holographic process is shown in Fig. 1. In the first step the hologram is formed by splitting the output from the laser into two beams; one is used to back-illuminate the model, while the other acts as a reference beam. The object beam wavefront is altered due to the presence of the model and combined with the known wavefront of the reference beam to form an interference pattern which is recorded on a photographic plate. After processing, this interference pattern acts as a diffraction grating which, when re-illuminated by the reference beam, will reconstruct the object wavefront. As shown in Fig. 1b, three orders are produced by the hologram--the two first orders which contain an image of the model and the zeroth order which does not.

In order to simplify the analysis, both the undisturbed object and the reference beams are assumed to be collimated, coherent, and monochromatic. The holographic plate is located normal to the object beam; and the reference beam has an angle of incidence of θ, as shown in Fig. 1. The reference beam is

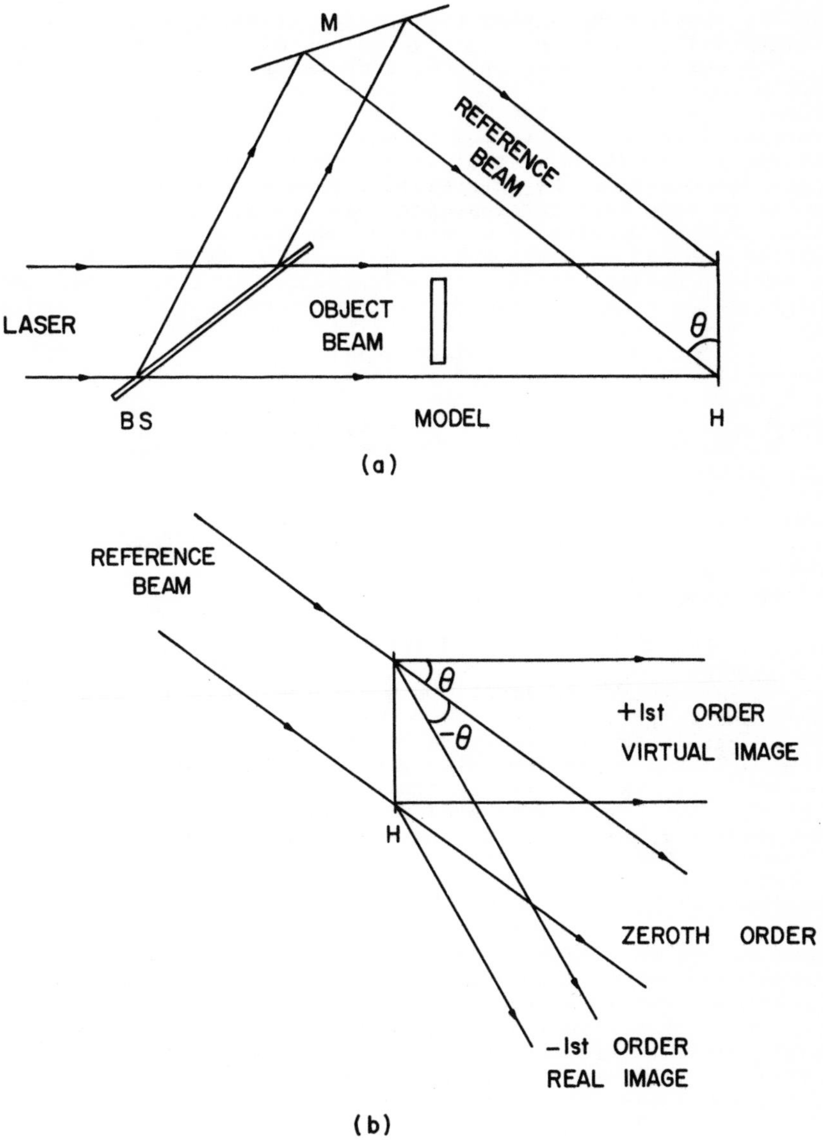

FIG. I SCHEMATIC DIAGRAM OF OPTICAL ARRANGEMENT FOR (a) HOLOGRAPHIC FORMATION, AND (b) RECONSTRUCTION PROCESS represented as

$$\vec{E}_R = \underset{\sim}{E}_R e^{-ikx \sin\theta} \tag{1}$$

where $\underset{\sim}{E}_R$ is the complex amplitude. The state of polarization will be expressed by this amplitude which has a role of primary importance in the analysis of birefringent material. The wave number is given by

$$k = \frac{2\pi}{\lambda} \tag{2}$$

where λ is the wavelength of the monochromatic light.

The object beam is represented by

$$\vec{E}_o = \underset{\sim}{E}_o \tag{3}$$

The total amplitude at the holographic plate is

$$\vec{E}_T = \underset{\sim}{E}_R e^{-ikx \sin\theta} + \underset{\sim}{E}_o \tag{4}$$

The intensity recorded by the film is given by

$$I = \vec{E}_T^{\dagger} \vec{E}_T \tag{5}$$

where $\dagger$ denotes the adjoint operator (i.e., the complex conjugate of the transpose).

The exposure is given by

$$\mathcal{E} = It \tag{6}$$

where t is the time interval for which the plate has received light intensity I.

At this stage the photographic plate may be processed, thereby permanently recording the interference pattern described by equation (5). If the plate is relocated and again illuminated by the reference beam, it acts as a diffraction grating. The intensity transmission function of such an amplitude grating may be written as

$$\tau = K(\mathcal{E})^{-\gamma} \tag{7}$$

where K and γ are constants which depend on the type of film used and the exposure time. It is more convenient to consider the film as a mapping of the intensity incident during the exposure into the complex amplitude transmitted after development. In view of this, we define an amplitude transmission function, $\mathfrak{T}$, which under certain restrictions can be shown[11] to equal the positive square root of τ. Likewise, the values of K and γ may be chosen without loss of generality[11], such that the amplitude transmission function may be written as

$$\mathfrak{T} = \mathcal{E} \tag{8}$$

If more than one exposure is made on the same plate, the amplitude transmission factor is given by their sum, i.e.,

$$\mathfrak{T}_2 = \mathcal{E}_1 + \mathcal{E}_2 \tag{9}$$

During the reconstruction process, the plate is illuminated by a beam, similar to the reference beam, which is denoted as

$$\vec{E}_{RC} = \underset{\sim}{E}_{RC} e^{-ikx \sin\theta} \tag{10}$$

The diffracted wavefronts are given by

$$\vec{E}_D = \mathfrak{T}\,\vec{E}_{RC} \tag{11}$$

Inserting equations (4), (5), and (6), this becomes

$$\begin{aligned}\vec{E}_D = t\{&\underset{\sim}{E}_R\underset{\sim}{E}_R^{\dagger} + \underset{\sim}{E}_o\underset{\sim}{E}_o^{\dagger} + \underset{\sim}{E}_R^{\dagger}\underset{\sim}{E}_o\, e^{+ikx\sin\theta} \\ &+ \underset{\sim}{E}_o^{\dagger}\underset{\sim}{E}_R\, e^{-ikx\sin\theta}\}\underset{\sim}{E}_{RC}\, e^{-ikx\sin\theta}\end{aligned} \tag{12}$$

If we limit our attention to the virtual image (i.e., the term which propagates in the same direction as the original object beam), the amplitude of the reconstructed wavefront is given by

$$\underset{\sim}{E}_V = t\,(\underset{\sim}{E}_R^{\dagger}\underset{\sim}{E}_o)\underset{\sim}{E}_{RC} \tag{13}$$

If a double exposure is used, the resulting virtual image wavefront is given by

$$\underset{\sim}{E}_V = [t_1(\underset{\sim}{E}_R^{\dagger}\underset{\sim}{E}_{o1}) + t_2(\underset{\sim}{E}_R^{\dagger}\underset{\sim}{E}_{o2})]\underset{\sim}{E}_{RC} \tag{14}$$

where t_1 and t_2 denote the exposure times during the first and second exposure. Note that the polarization of the diffracted beam is identical to that of the reconstruction beam.

The intensity in the virtual image is given by

$$I_V = \underset{\sim}{E}_V^{\dagger}\underset{\sim}{E}_V \tag{15}$$

Real-Time Holographic Interferometry

An important special case of holographic interferometry is real-time interferometry. In this case the hologram records the first exposure and reconstructs the wavefront associated with the virtual image as indicated by equation (13). The model is then loaded and the wavefront from the loaded model plus the diffracted virtual image wavefront from the unloaded model combine to form the desired interference pattern. In this case the real-time wavefront is given by

$$\underset{\sim}{E}_{RT} = t_1(\underset{\sim}{E}_R^{\dagger}\underset{\sim}{E}_{o1})\underset{\sim}{E}_R + \underset{\sim}{E}_{o2} \tag{16}$$

Note the difference between expressions (14) and (16). For the double exposure technique the two wavefronts which are compared are proportional to the intensity during each exposure and have the same polarization, determined solely by the reconstruction beam. For real-time holography the diffracted beam is proportional to the intensity which existed during the first exposure and is compared to the existing wavefront. The polarization states of the two wavefronts may not be the same. The intensity is given by equation (5).

STRESS-OPTIC LAW

Up to this point the discussion has dealt only with holography and not specifically with its application to holographic photoelasticity. The relationship between the stress in the model and the intensity in the reconstructed image of the hologram will now be developed.

The photoelastic method utilizes materials which exhibit stress induced birefringence. This effect is shown in Fig. 2. A ray of plane polarized light incident upon the stressed model is broken down into two components. The two components propagate through the model with different velocities, hence, the exiting ray is elliptically polarized. The relationship between the velocity of propagation of each component and the stress state is given by the Maxwell-Neumann stress optic law.

$$n_1 - n_o = A\sigma_1 + B\sigma_2$$
$$n_2 - n_o = B\sigma_1 + A\sigma_2 \qquad (18)$$

where n_o = index of refraction of unstressed model
n_1 and n_2 = indices of refraction for the stressed model for light polarized in directions parallel to the principal stresses σ_1 and σ_2

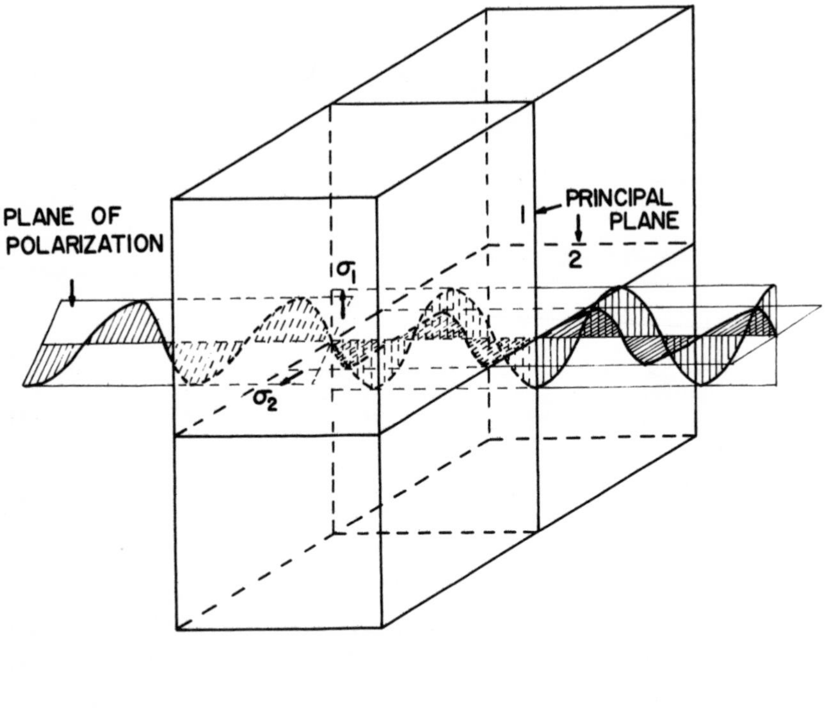

FIG. 2 SCHEMATIC REPRESENTATION OF LIGHT PROPAGATION THROUGH A BIREFRINGENT MATERIAL. LINEARLY POLARIZED LIGHT IS RESOLVED INTO COMPONENTS IN THE PRINCIPAL STRESS DIRECTIONS, AND PROPAGATES WITH A VELOCITY DETERMINED BY THE MAGNITUDE OF THE PRINCIPAL STRESS COMPONENT.

Let the phase change of the ray due to the unstressed model be denoted by α, and α_1 and α_2 denote the phase changes in the stressed model in the directions σ_1 and σ_2. These are given by

$$\alpha = \frac{2\pi}{\lambda}(n_o - 1)t$$

$$\alpha_1 = \frac{2\pi}{\lambda}[n_1 t' + 1(t - t')] \qquad (19)$$

$$\alpha_2 = \frac{2\pi}{\lambda}[n_2 t' + 1(t - t')]$$

where t is the initial thickness of the model
t' is the final thickness of the model.
If the model is in a state of plane stress, i.e., the stress component in the thickness direction is zero, from the stress-strain relationship

$$t' = t - \frac{\nu}{E}(\sigma_1 + \sigma_2) \qquad (20)$$

where E = Young's Modulus
ν = Poisson's Ratio
In order to derive the expression for the light intensity in the reconstructed virtual image for various arrangements of the optical components, it will be convenient to use the Jones matrix method of representation[12].

COMBINED ISOCHROMATIC-ISOPACHIC FRINGE PATTERN

Consider the case of circularly polarized light in both the reference and object beams. The reference and undisturbed object beam are written as

$$\underset{\sim}{E}_R = \frac{\sqrt{2}}{2}\begin{bmatrix} i \\ 1 \end{bmatrix}, \quad E_o = \frac{\sqrt{2}}{2}\begin{bmatrix} i \\ 1 \end{bmatrix}. \qquad (21)$$

The unloaded model is assumed to be optical isotropic; hence, the matrix representing it may be written as

$$M_u = e^{-i\alpha}\begin{bmatrix} 1 & 0 \\ 0 & 1 \end{bmatrix}, \qquad (22)$$

The loaded model may be represented by

$$M_s = \begin{bmatrix} m_{11} & m_{12} \\ m_{12} & m_{22} \end{bmatrix} \qquad (23)$$

where

$$m_{11} = \cos^2\beta\, e^{-i\alpha_1} + \sin^2\beta\, e^{-i\alpha_2}$$

$$m_{12} = m_{21} = \cos\beta \sin\beta\,(e^{-i\alpha 1} - e^{i\alpha 2})$$

$$m_{22} = \cos^2\beta\, e^{-i\alpha_2} + \sin^2\beta\, e^{-i\alpha_1}$$

where β is the angle between one principal stress axis and the horizontal coordinate axis. This is commonly called the isoclinic angle, and the locus of points where β is constant are called isoclinics.

The holographic arrangement is the same as shown in Fig. 1. The expression for the final object beam is obtained by multiplication of the vector representing the original object beam by the various matrices representing each element in the order in which the beam passes through that element. In this case the final object beam for the unstressed model is given by

$$\tilde{E}_{o1} = M_u \tilde{E}_o \tag{24}$$

Similarly, for the stressed model

$$\tilde{E}_{o2} = M_s \tilde{E}_o \tag{25}$$

and the amplitude of the wavefront of the reconstructed virtual image for the double exposure hologram is given by (for equal unit exposure times)

$$\tilde{E}_v = [\tilde{E}_R^{\dagger} M_u \tilde{E}_o + \tilde{E}_R^{\dagger} M_s \tilde{E}_o]\tilde{E}_{RC} \tag{26}$$

The intensity is given by equation (15). If equations (21), (22), and (23) are substituted into equation (26), the resulting expression is

$$I = \frac{3}{2} + \cos(\alpha - \alpha_1) + \cos(\alpha - \alpha_2) + \frac{1}{2}\cos(\alpha_1 - \alpha_2) \tag{27}$$

By means of equations (18) and (19), and after some simplification, this becomes

$$I = 1 + 2\cos\frac{\pi t}{\lambda} C(\sigma_1 - \sigma_2) \cdot \cos\frac{\pi t}{\lambda}(A' + B')(\sigma_1 + \sigma_2) + \cos^2\frac{\pi t}{\lambda} C(\sigma_1 - \sigma_2) \tag{28}$$

where

$$A' = A - \frac{\nu}{E}(n_o - n)$$

$$B' = B - \frac{\nu}{E}(n_o - n)$$

$$C = A' - B'$$

and terms of the order ν/E have been neglected relative to terms of order one in expression (28).

The locus of points where $\sigma 1 + \sigma 2$ = a constant are known as isopachics; points where $\sigma 1 - \sigma 2$ = a constant are known as isochromatics. This intensity pattern is a function of both the isochromatic and isopachic.

The locus of points where

$$\frac{\pi t}{\lambda} C(\sigma_1 - \sigma_2) = m\pi \quad m = \text{integer} \tag{29}$$

corresponds to a light isochromatic fringe in a standard light-field photoelastic pattern. However, in this case, the light isochromatic is modulated by the isopachic pattern, given by

$$I = 2 \pm 2\cos\frac{\pi t}{\lambda}(A' + B')(\sigma_1 + \sigma_2) \tag{30}$$

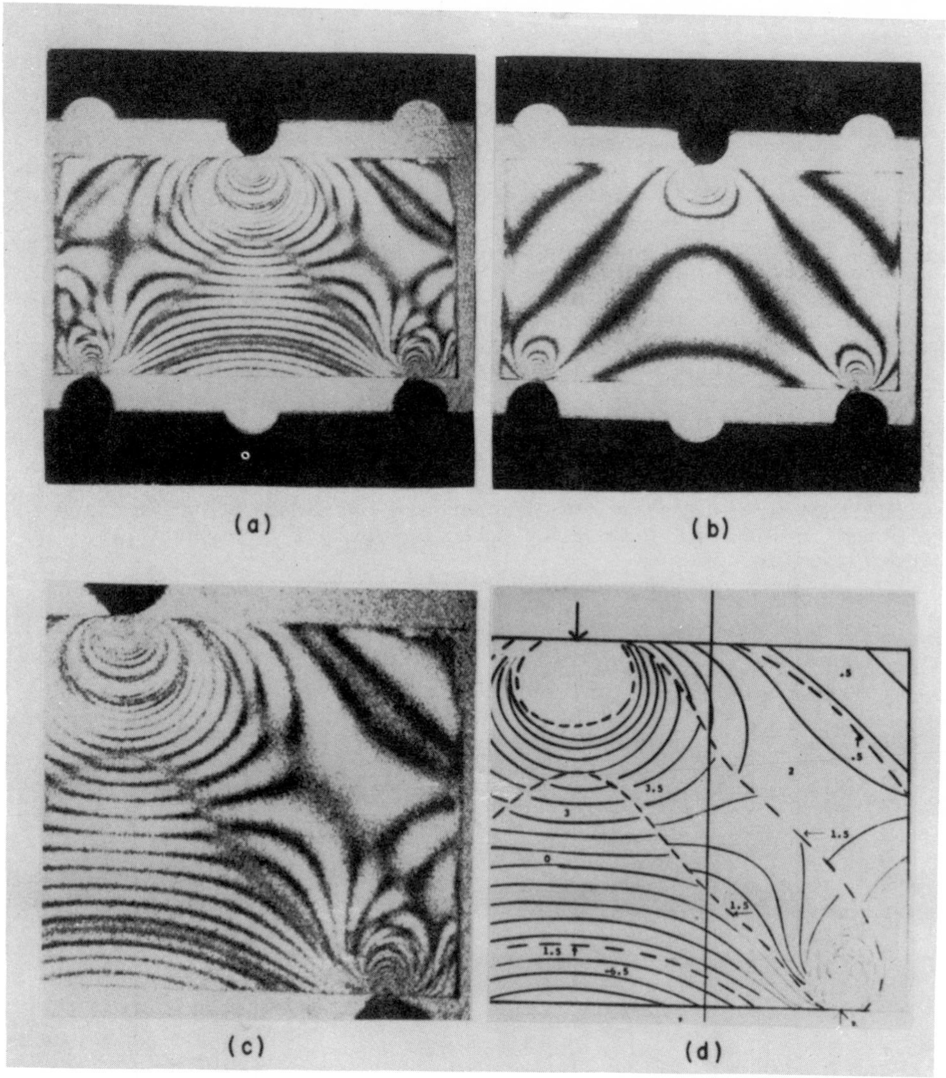

FIG. 3 DEEP BEAM WITH CENTRAL CONCENTRATED LOAD (a) RECONSTRUCTED VIRTUAL IMAGE SHOWING COMBINED FRINGE PATTERN (b) ISOCHROMATIC PATTERN (c) ENLARGED VIEW OF COMBINED PATTERN (d) DIAGRAM SHOWING FRINGE ORDER.

Points where

$$\frac{\pi t}{\lambda} C(\sigma_1 - \sigma_2) = \left(\frac{2m+1}{2}\right)\pi \tag{31}$$

correspond to the dark isochromatic fringe and have in this case the intensity

$$I = 1 , \tag{32}$$

which, from equation (30), is seen to be a half-tone fringe. Furthermore, from equation (31), it is seen that, as the isopachic fringes intersect the isochromatic fringes, their intensity reverses from light to dark and vice versa.

An example of this type of fringe pattern is shown in Fig. 3. This shows a deep beam with a central concentrated load. The fringe pattern in the reconstructed virtual image is shown; examination of details of this pattern show all of the effects discussed above.

Both the sum and difference of the principal stresses can be determined from the value of the isochromatic and isopachic fringes. Hence, the magnitude of the stress state at any point in the model can be readily determined. The stress components along the vertical line of Fig. 3d have been determined and are plotted in Fig. 4. Comparison with results of reference [13] shows good agreement.

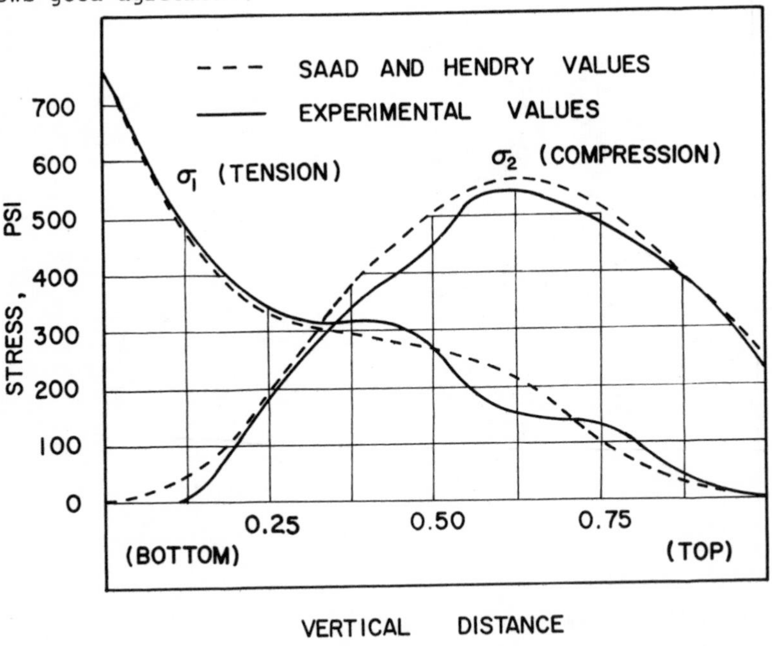

FIG. 4 PLOT OF σ_1 AND σ_2 FOR BEAM WITH W=2/3L.

The expression given by equation (28) is similar to one obtained by Nisida and Saito for interferometric photoelasticity using a Mach-Zender interferometer. The only difference is the third term that appears in equation (28). This term represents the isochromatic pattern which implies an interference between the wavefronts associated with the two principal directions and is not present in the expression for classical interferometry. The origin of this term may be explained by the following discussion. During the second exposure of the double exposure hologram, the wavefront incident upon the stressed model was broken down into two orthogonal polarization states. Associated with each of these states is a wavefront which has some component in a direction parallel to the polarization state of the reference beam. This component of each wavefront forms an interference pattern in the hologram. Upon reconstruction, each interference pattern reconstructs its own wavefront, but now each has a state of polarization determined by the reconstruction beam. Whereas, during the formation process, these wavefronts had orthogonal states of polarization and could not interfere, they now have identical polarization states and the resulting interference gives rise to this third term.

For a real-time hologram in which the reference exposure was of the unstressed model, the above argument does not apply and the expression should be identical to that of a classical interferometry. This can be shown by substituting equation (21), and the expanded forms of equations (24) and (25) into equation (16). The resulting expression is

$$I_{RT} = 1 + \cos(\alpha - \alpha_1) + \cos(\alpha - \alpha_2) \tag{33}$$

where the constants and exposure time have been chosen such that the amplitude of the diffracted wavefront is equal to that of the wavefront for the model. Upon substitution of equation (18) and (19) into this expression, it becomes

$$I_{RT} = 1 + 2\cos\frac{\pi t}{\lambda} C(\sigma_1 - \sigma_2) \cdot \cos\frac{\pi t}{\lambda}(A' + B')(\sigma_1 + \sigma_2) \tag{34}$$

which is identical to the expression obtained by Nisida and Saito.

SEPARATION OF PRINCIPAL STRESSES

In the preceding example, the dark fringes were denoted as either isochromatics or isopachics. Examination of equation (28) shows that, since the second term represents the cross modulation of these two functions the nulls of the total expression are not in general the nulls of either of these functions. Although in most cases this does not result in large errors in analysis due to the much higher spatial frequency of the isopachics than the isochromatics, it can lead to difficulty in interpretation of the fringe pattern. This effect has been studied in detail by Holloway[8], Stanford and Durelli[9], and O'Regan and Dudderar[10].

The spatial frequency of the isochromatic and isopachic functions are governed both by material constants of the model and the stress distribution. The stress distribution determines their orientation. It has been shown[8,9,10] that the most critical case is when the spatial frequency of both functions are approximately equal and the fringes are nearly parallel. A graphic example of the difficulty of interpretation is shown in Figs. (5) and (6). Fig. (5) shows a computer simulated isochromatic-isopachic fringe pattern of a disk loading in diametral compression. Sanford[9], using the analytical solution for the disk and equation (28), has generated these simulated fringe patterns using an analog computer. A plot of the light intensity along the horizontal radius is shown in Fig. (6). Two difficulties with interpretation may occur, (a) identification of the fringe order, and (b) a shift in location of a null point.

Several methods of separating the two families of fringes have been proposed. The most direct method is to obtain a separate isochromatic pattern which is then used in conjunction with the combined pattern. This may easily be obtained in either a double exposure or real-time hologram by simply placing a mask

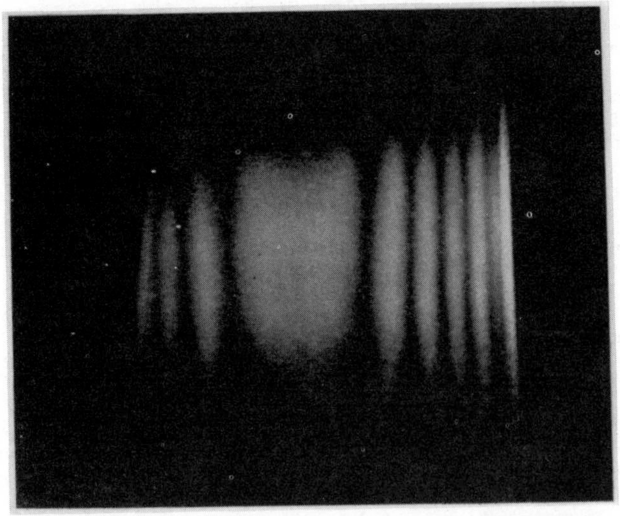

FIG. 5 COMPUTER SIMULATED COMBINED FRINGE PATTERN OF CIRCULAR DISK IN DIAMETRAL COMPRESSION. (COURTESY OF R. J. SANFORD.)

over a portion of the hologram during the first exposure. The unmasked portion recorded the entire unloaded image due to the well known distribution property of the hologram. The mask is removed during the second exposure and the entire plate exposed. Those portions of the hologram which were unmasked during the first exposure will have recorded the combined interference pattern while the remaining portions will have recorded only the isochromatic pattern. By means of equation (28) and these two fringe patterns, the individual families may be obtained. This technique has been demonstrated by Holloway[8] for dynamic applications and Hovanesion[14] for thermal stress problems.

Another method suggested by Sciammarella and Quintanilla[15] involves the determination of the two families of absolute retardation fringes, i.e., the families corresponding to α_1 and α_2. These two families, together with the isochromatic pattern, allow a semi-graphical, trial and error type procedure to be used for the desired separation.

A more general technique has been suggested by Dudderar and O'Regan[10]. This technique physically separates the two families on separate planes by means of an optical setup similar to that shown in Fig. 7. The object beam first passes through the model, and then through an optical rotator which rotates the plane of polarization of the light by 90° on a double pass. The beam is reflected by a partially transmitting mirror and then retraces its path through the rotator and model. Due to the optical rotator, the phase change due to the σ_1 and σ_2 axes are now interchanged. The beam is then directed onto the holographic plate by means of a beam splitter. It combines with the reference beam to form a hologram in the standard fashion.

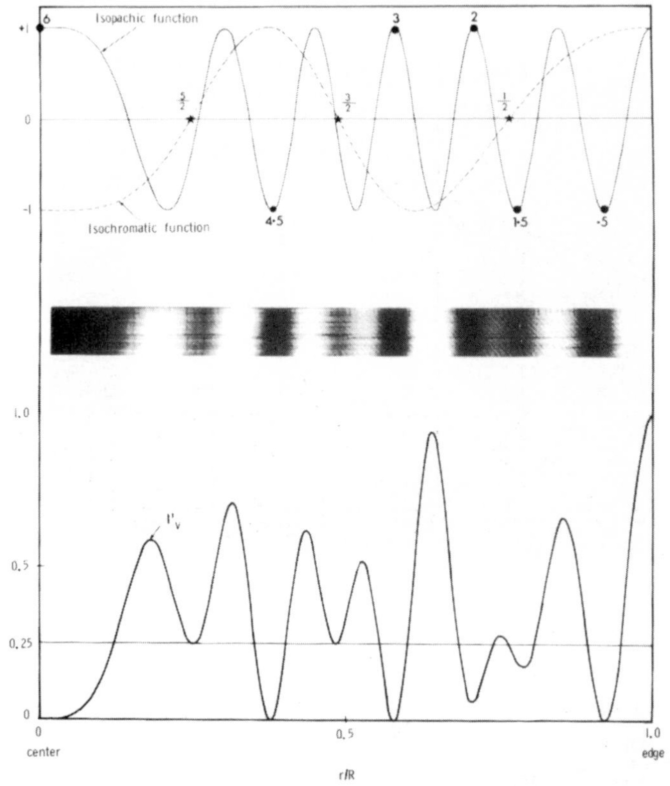

FIG. 6 PLOT OF LIGHT INTENSITY ALONG HORIZONTAL RADIUS OF DISK. (COURTESY OF R. J. SANFORD)

Assume that the original object beam and reference are left circularly polarized. The rotator will have a matrix of the form

$$R = \begin{bmatrix} 0 & 1 \\ -1 & 0 \end{bmatrix} \tag{35}$$

for light which has made a double pass by retracing its path. The object beam for the unstressed model is given by

$$\underset{\sim}{E}_{o1} = e^{-i2\alpha} \begin{bmatrix} 1 \\ -i \end{bmatrix} \tag{36}$$

For the stressed model the final object beam is given by

$$\underset{\sim}{E}_{o2} = M_L \, R \, M_L \, \underset{\sim}{E}_o \tag{37}$$

Since the matrix for the model is symmetric, it may pre-multiply the light vector exiting from the rotator, and the result will be the same as if it were post-multiplied in the fashion suggested by Jones[12]. With this arrangement, the rotator is left in place for both exposures and the resulting intensity expression is given by

$$I = 1 + \cos \frac{2\pi t}{\lambda} (A' + B') (\sigma_1 + \sigma_2) \tag{38}$$

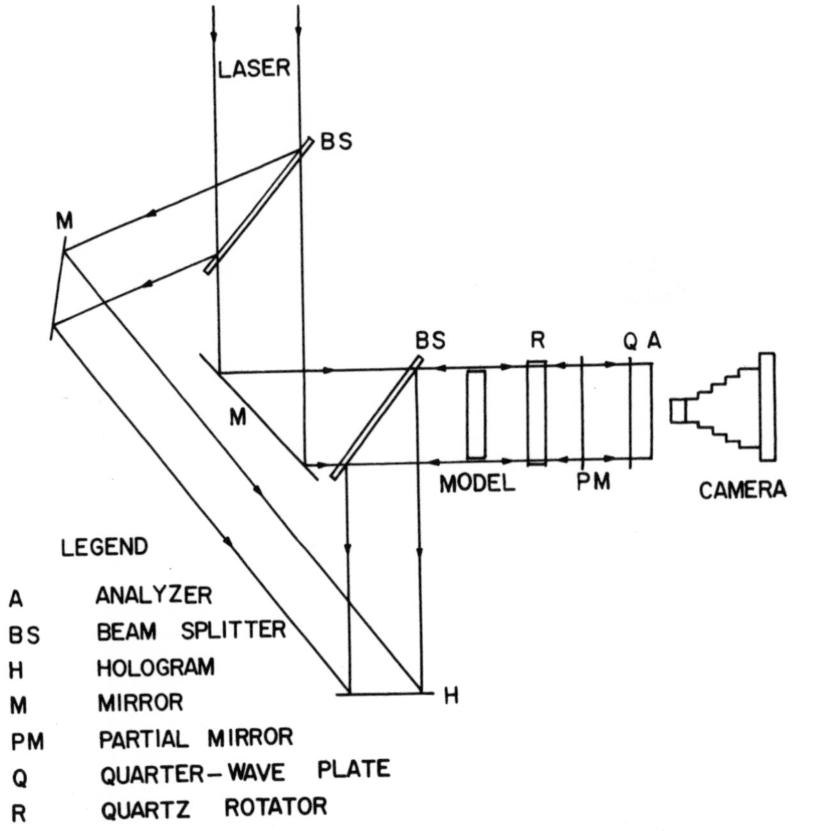

FIG. 7 SCHEMATIC DIAGRAM OF OPTICAL ARRANGEMENT FOR SEPARATION OF COMBINED FRINGE PATTERN.

Hence, only the isopachic fringe pattern is present and the sensitivity is twice that of the normal procedure. The isochromatic pattern is easily determined by placing a quarter-wave plate and analyzer after the partial mirror. A photograph taken during the second exposure will yield a conventional isochromatic pattern.

ISOCLINIC DETERMINATION

A complete determination of the stress states requires a knowledge of the direction of the principal stresses as well as their magnitudes. This is accomplished in photo-elasticity by determining the entire family of isoclinic fringes. A plane polarized beam illuminates the loaded model and a plane polarize-orineted at 90° to this plane is used as an analyzer. Using equation (23) this can easily be shown to yield the following expression for the intensity in the image.

$$I = 4\sin^2 2\beta \sin^2 \frac{\pi t}{\lambda} C(\sigma_1 - \sigma_2) \tag{39}$$

The intensity is zero when $2\beta = n\pi$; of interest here are $\beta = 0$, or $\pi/2$, i.e., when one of the principal stress components is parallel and the other perpendicular to the axis of the analyzer. By varying the angle β from zero through 90° the isoclinic fringes will traverse the entire model. Therefore, the principal stress directions at each point are known.

However, for dynamic problems it is not practical to alter the plane of polarization for each instantaneous determination of the stress state. This generally requires an order of magnitude increase in speed and complexity of the equipment.

An alternate approach is to record and reconstruct the state of polarization of the wavefront from the loaded model. It is then possible to obtain the complete family of isoclinics for each instantaneous loading state. This may be accomplished by using two orthogonally polarized reference beams to interfere with the elliptically polarized object beam. At each point the object beam is decomposed into the orthogonal polarization states corresponding to those of the two reference beams, and two interference patterns are recorded. A schematic of the optical arrangement which has been used is shown in Fig. 8. It can be shown[6] that, in this case, there are eight wavefronts reconstructed rather than the four as indicated by equation (12). Four crosstalk images will be formed, two real and two virtual. These images result from the wavefront formed by the reference beam of one polarization state diffracting light from the interference pattern formed by the reference beam of the orthogonal state of polarization. In Fig. 8 the optics are arranged such that these images are spatially separated and do not overlap.

If the reconstructed virtual wavefronts are to add vectorially to yield the object's original state of polarization, the phase relationship between the reconstructed components must be the same as that between the components of the original object wavefront. This implies that it is necessary to maintain the polarization and location of the reference beams with respect to the holograph from the formation process through the reconstruction process. This reconstructed wavefront may then be viewed through an analyzer at various isoclinic angles to obtain the desired information.

A necessary modification to the conventional isoclinic pattern is required in that the model must be illuminated with circularly polarized light and viewed with a linear analyzer. This is necessary to avoid the introduction of a specific bias in polarization direction at the outset.

The intensity pattern that results from this arrangement can easily be shown to be[6].

$$I = 1 + \sin 2\beta \sin(\alpha_1 - \alpha_2). \qquad (40)$$

when $\beta = 0$, i.e., when the axis of the analyzer is the same as a principal axis, then $I = 1$ or half the maximum. Thus, the isoclinics for this arrangement are grey or half-tone fringes. Also, since the term $\sin(\alpha_1 - \alpha_2)$ is modulated by the factor $\sin(2\beta)$, the isochromatics change from light to dark and vice versa as they cross isoclinics. Both of these effects are seen in Fig. 9.

It must be noted here that the restrictions imposed by this method are much more stringent than even those of real-time holography. A half wavelength shift, which is normally acceptable, would result in 90° of phase error for this method; this is at least ten times the acceptable error. An even larger problem is the requirement that the phase of the two reference beams remain constant at all points on the holographic plane from the formation through the reconstruction phase. In practice, emulsion shrinkage or changes in room temperature on the order of only a few degrees are sufficient to cause a complete cycle in fringe shift. For the experiment illustrated by Fig. 9, after emulsion shrinkage was minimized, changes in room temperature were utilized to counteract

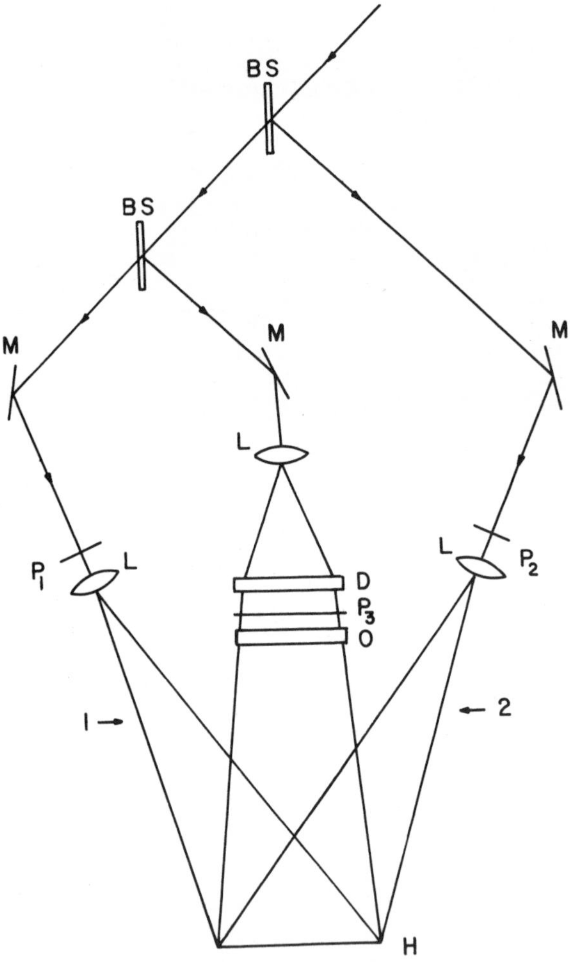

FIG. 8 SCHEMATIC DIAGRAM OF OPTICAL ARRANGEMENT USED IN RECORDING POLARIZATION. OBJECT, O, OF WHICH HOLOGRAM, H, IS TO BE FORMED IS ILLUMINATED BY DIFFUSED CIRCULARLY POLARIZED LIGHT BY VIRTUE OF DIFFUSER, D, AND POLARIZER P_3. ORTHOGONALLY POLARIZED REFERENCE BEAMS 1 AND 2 ARE PRODUCED BY POLARIZERS P_1 AND P_2.

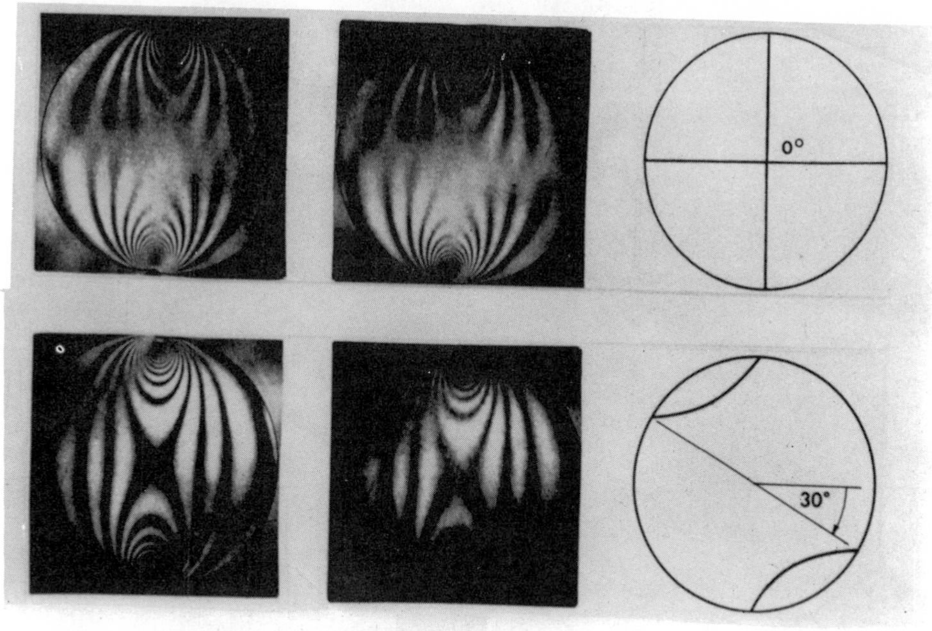

(a) OBJECT (b) HOLOGRAPH (c) THEORETICAL ISOCLINICS

FIG. 9 ISOCLINICS OBTAINED A POSTERIORI FOR A CIRCULAR DISK UNDER DIAMETRAL COMPRESSION.

the remaining phase error due to emulsion shrinkage.

APPLICATIONS

The major applications of holographic photoelasticity to date have dealt with the solution of two-dimensional plane stress problems similar to the one illustrated by Figs. 3 and 4. Many of these problems are associated with design; others are associated with the determination of the two-dimensional stress distribution in the vicinity of cracks, or adjacent to the boundary of two dissimilar materials. The latter example is for work in composite material where a detailed knowledge of the load transfer between the two materials is desired.

Of current interest is the extension of this method into areas where other techniques can not adequately handle the problems encountered. Two of these areas are (a) dynamic problems, and (b) three-dimensional analysis.

(a) Dynamic Problems

Dynamic Problems are defined as problems involving the determination of the stress distribution associated with stress wave propagation. The only requirement for the application of holographic photoelasticity to dynamic problems is that the exposure time used to form the hologram must be sufficiently fast to arrest any motion. This requirement, most easily met using a giant-pulsed ruby laser, which typically has a light pulse duration of the order of 10 nanoseconds. A double exposure technique is generally used

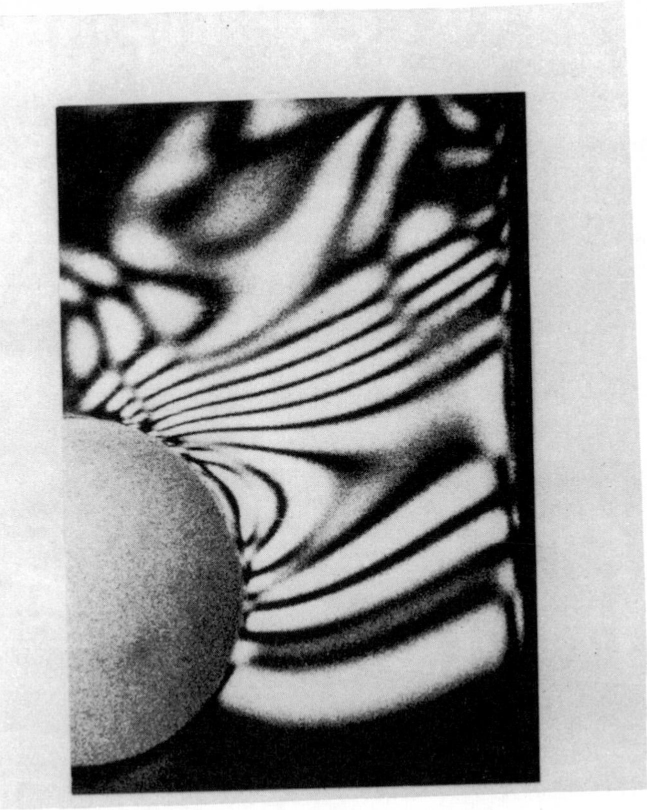

FIG. 10 DYNAMIC COMBINED FRINGE PATTERN. DOUBLE EXPOSURE METHOD WITH TIME INTERVAL OF 54μ SECOND. (COURTESY OF D. C. HOLLOWAY AND C. E. TAYLOR.)

with the first exposure being that of the unloaded model. This exposure may be made at any time prior to application of the load, the only requirement being that no motion, other than that due to the load, should take place between the two exposures. This is generally not a stringent requirement, but in many cases it is best met by having the two exposures occur with the minimum time interval possible.

An example of this type of application is shown in Fig. 10. This shows a rectangular plate with a centrally located circular hole. The plate is loaded by an explosive load placed on the top. Figure 10 shows the stress wave propagation around the circular hole. The first exposure was made just prior to the detonation of the load and the second 54 μsec later. Both isochromatic and isopachic fringe orders may in principle be determined at each point and the magnitude of principal stresses obtained. Since this is not possible using conventional photoelastic techniques, this represents an important application of holographic photoelasticity.

(b) Three-Dimensional Problems

Up to this point, only two-dimensional problems have been considered. For these problems the complete solution required the determination of three unknowns at each point. For three-dimensional problems the number of unknowns increases to six. The solution to this type of problem is notoriously difficult; in fact, few solutions for the general three-dimensional problem have been obtained by any means.

Several techniques have been used in photoelasticity, none

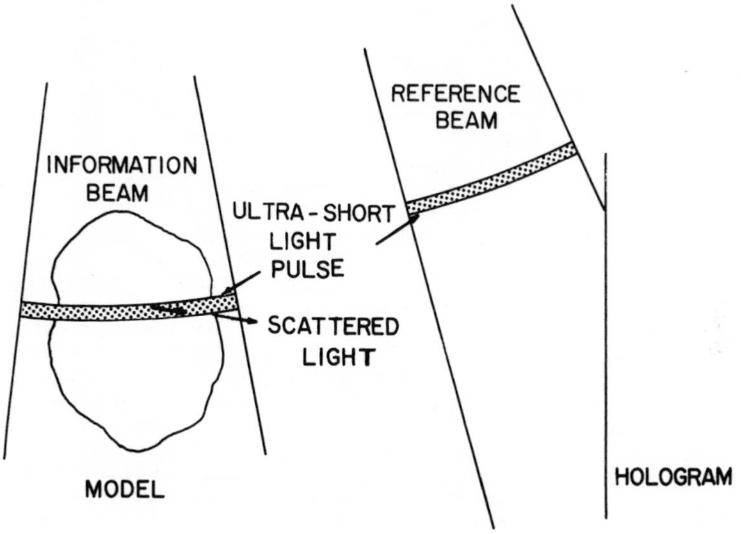

(a) FORMATION PROCESS UTILIZING PICOSECOND LIGHT PULSE AND SCATTERED LIGHT.

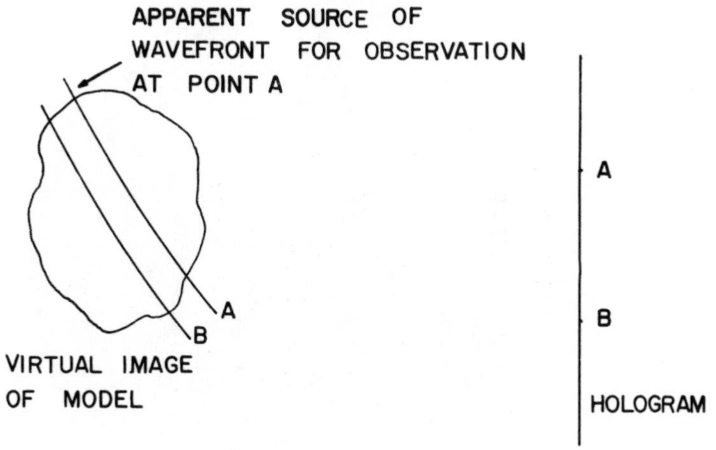

(b) RECONSTRUCTION PROCESS

FIG. 11 PICOSECOND HOLOGRAPHIC THREE - DIMENSIONAL PHOTOELASTIC TECHNIQUE.

of which are completely satisfactory. Perhaps one of the better known techniques is the stress "freezing" technique. This method involves loading the model at an elevated temperature and maintaining the load as the temperature is decreased. Certain birefringent materials exhibit a memory that allows optical effects induced by stress above some transition temperature to be permanently retained if the load is maintained as the temperature is decreased to a value less than the transition point.

A model subjected to this type of temperature cycle may then be cut into slices and analyzed. Nisida and Saito[3] suggested the use of interferometric photoelasticity to analyze each slice. Nisida, Saito, and Sawa[16] demonstrated the feasibility of the method for certain classes of problems but showed that with a single slice only four unknowns could be readily determined for each point. The general three-dimensional problem requires that two models be made and each point contained in two slices taken in different directions, e.g., orthogonal slices. Holographic interferometry has been used[17] to replace the Mach-Zender interferometry; however, the basic limitation discussed in reference [16] and briefly mentioned above still remains.

A potentially more versatile method has been proposed by the author and research on this method is currently under way. The method combines scattered light photoelasticity and picosecond holographic interferometry. The light source required for this application is a mode-locked laser. With present day mode-locking techniques[18], it is possible to generate light pulses that are 0.3 mm in length or shorter. The suggested method is shown in Fig. 11. A single mode-locked pulse is considered, which might be one of a train of pulses from either a pulsed or cw mode-locked laser. The pulse is divided by a beam splitter to form both object and reference beams for the holographic process. As the object beam propagates through the transparent model, a certain portion of the beam will be scattered in the direction of the holographic

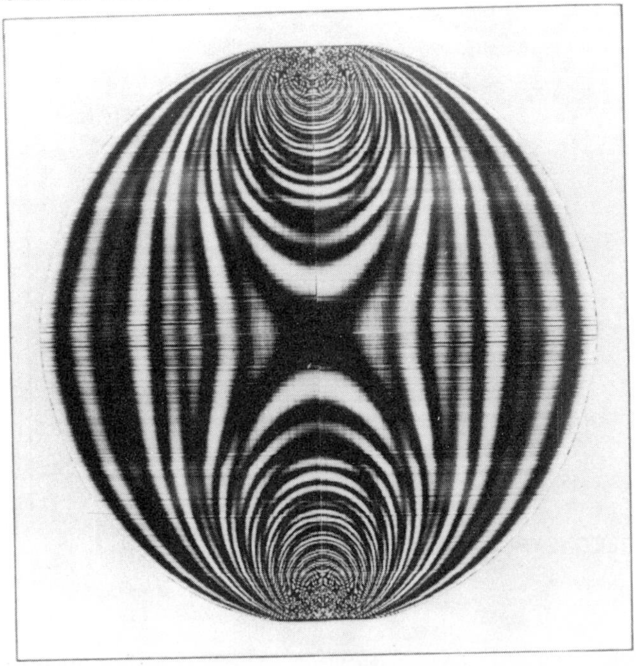

FIG. 12 SCATTERED LIGHT FRINGE PATTERN OF A SECTION OF A BEAM IN PURE BENDING. CENTRAL PLANE OF BEAM IS INCLINED AT 45° TO THE IMAGE PLANE.

plate. The reference beam sweeps across the holographic plate, and interference with the scattered light can only occur when the two beams overlap. This implies an equal time of arrival principle for light scattered by some portions of the model to each point on the hologram. This in turn defines some scattering surface in the model for each point on the hologram. This is indicated in Fig. 11b by surface A corresponding to point A. During the reconstruction process, if the hologram is viewed from point A, the wavefront that is reconstructed will have been scattered from surface A; the same correspondence holds for point B and surface B. If an interferometric technique is used, then the integrated birefringence from surface A will be recorded at point A and similarly with point B, etc. Hence, the birefringence due to the material between surfaces A and B may be obtained by subtracting the wavefront from point A from that of point B. This subtraction process may be accomplished optically, and the net result is the same as if the model had been "optically sliced". If the two holographs are made simultaneously from two different positions, then each point in the body may be analyzed as part of two independent slices. The information thus obtained will be sufficient to yield the six unknowns required for each point. The method would be applicable to either static or dynamic problems.

Some of the very early results in this research area are shown in Fig. 12. The purpose of this test was merely to confirm that the scattered light technique could be adapted for use in holography. Figure 12 shows the reconstructed virtual image of a beam in constant bending. In this case the light source used was a cw laser.

SUMMARY

Although the application of holography to photoelasticity is relatively new, a great deal of progress has been made. This is due primarily to the background developed in interferometric photoelasticity and moiré analysis. Holography has allowed the concepts and techniques developed there to both be extended into new areas and reduced in difficulty to a point where they are more useful. Dynamic problems are now tractable with a reasonable amount of effort. Although new methods have been prepared for three-dimensional problems, at present much work remains to be accomplished.

ACKNOWLEDGEMENT

The author wishes to acknowledge the support of NSF Grant #GK-22676, and the able assistance of Young Jai Lee in the preparation of the figures for this manuscript.

REFERENCES

[1] H. Favre, "Sur une Nouvelle Méthod Optique de Determination des Tensions Interieures," Rev. d'Optique, 8, pp. 193-213, 241-261, 289-307, 1929.

[2] D. Post, "The Generic Nature of the Absolute-Retardation Method in Photoelasticity," Exp. Mech., 7(6), June 1967.

[3] M. Nisida and H. Saito, "A New Interferometric Method of Two-Dimensional Stress Analysis," Exp. Mech., 4(12), pp. 366-376 December 1964.

[4] M. E. Fourney, "Application of Holography to Photoelasticity," Exp. Mech., pp. 33-38, January 1968.

[5] J. D. Hovanesion, V. Brcic, and R. L. Powell, "A New Experimental Stress-Optic Method: Stress-Holo-Interferometry," Exp. Mech., 8(8), pp. 362-368, August 1968.

[6] M. E. Fourney and K. V. Mate, "Further Applications of Holography to Photoelasticity," Exp. Mech., 10(5), pp. 177-188,

May 1970.

[7] V. E. Hosp and G. Wutze, "The Application of Holography in Plane Photoelasticity," Materialprüfung, 11(12) pp. 409-415, 1969. "Holographic Determination of the Principal Stresses in Plane Models," Materialprüfung, 12(1), pp. 13-22, 1970.

[8] D. C. Holloway, "Holography and the Application to Photoelasticity," T.&A.M. Report No. 329, Univ. of Ill., Urbana, Illinois, June 1969.

[9] R. J. Sanford and A. J. Durelli, "Interpretation of Fringes in Stress-Holo-Interferometry," Exp. Mech., 11(4), pp. 161-166, April 1971.

[10] R. O'Regan and T. D. Dudderar, "A New Holographic Interferometer for Stress Analysis," presented 1971 SESA Spring Meeting, May 1971, SESA Paper #1792.

[11] Joseph W. Goodman, Introduction to Fourier Optics, McGraw-Hill, New York, 1968.

[12] R. C. Jones, "New Calculus for the Treatment of Optical Systems," J. Opt. Soc. Amer.,
Part I, 31, pp. 488, 1941.
Part II (with H. Hurwitz), 31, p. 493, 1941.
Part III, 31, p. 500, 1941.
Part IV, 32, p. 486, 1942.
Part V, 37, p. 107, 1947.
Part VI, 37, p. 110, 1947.
Part VII, 38, 0. 671, 1948.

[13] S. Saad and A. W. Hendry, "Stresses in a Deep Beam with Central Concentrated Load," Exp. Mech., 1(5), pp. 192-198, May 1961.

[14] J. D. Hovanesion, "Strength-Weight Optimization of Sprag Profiles through Hologram Interferometry," presented 1970 SESA Spring Meeting, May 1970.

[15] C. A. Sciammerella and G. Quintanilla, "Techniques for the Determination of Absolute Retardation in Photoelasticity," presented 1970 SESA Fall Meeting, October 1970, SESA Paper #1719.

[16] M. Nisida, H. Saito, and Y. Sawa, "Application of Interferometric Method to Three-Dimensional Stress Analysis." Scientific Papers of the Institute of Physical and Chemical Research, (Saitama, Japan), 63(2), pp. 25-35, 1969.

[17] S. K. Dhir and H. A. Peterson, "An Application of Holography to Complete Stress Analysis of Photoelastic Models," presented 1971 SESA Spring Meeting, May 1971.

[18] A. DeMaria, D. Stetser and W. Glen, "Ultra-Short Light Pulses," Science, 156, p. 3782, 1967.

OPTICAL CORRELATION FOR REAL-TIME STRAIN MEASUREMENTS

E. Marom, T. Sawatari, and R. K. Mueller
Bendix Research Laboratories
Southfield, Michigan 48076

ABSTRACT

Two methods are described for measuring mechanical strain in real time using an optical correlation technique. In the first method, a coded matched-filter hologram is used, by which a strained object is transformed to a simple geometrical pattern. The strain is then evaluated from the deformed pattern. With the second method, strain is determined by well-established image-image correlation methods using incoherent illumination, where two photographs (one is the unstrained reference object and the other the strained object) are directly compared and the strain is plotted out. Experimental results based on the second method are presented.

INTRODUCTION

The application of optical techniques to experimental mechanics has been investigated for a long time. The best-known techniques are (1) photoelastic methods, (2) interferometric methods, and (3) moiré techniques. The photoelastic method is an old well-established art. However, it has the disadvantage that it requires a model made from transparent material which generates birefringence characteristics under stressed circumstances. Classical interferometry had a similar limitation; however, with the recent advent of laser holography, holographic interferometry is becoming a powerful new tool for strain analysis. The reasons for this are its applicability to opaque objects and its capability for real-time measurement. Sollid[1] pointed out that with three or more simultaneous holographic measurements, it is possible to analyze general three-dimensional displacement problems. However, the numerical computation becomes quite involved and extreme precision is required in positioning the holograms.

Another useful technique for the strain measurement is the moiré method[2] (otherwise known as mechanical interferometry). This analog type method eliminates complicated numerical processing and seems especially promising for in-plane strain measurement. It has a drawback, however, in that a high-frequency periodic pattern must be engraved on the surface of the object examined.

The techniques described in this paper may resolve some of the difficulties inherent in the strain measurement methods mentioned above. These techniques are based on the use of optical correlation, which may be obtained in one of two ways: one is a matched filter correlation and direct image-image correlation.

The application of the former technique to real-time strain measurement has been suggested by E. Marom and R. K. Mueller.[3] It may be worthwhile to review the method of E. Marom and R. K. Mueller before we introduce our techniques. The basic concept underlying strain measurement by correlation is that if an object is stressed linearly and produces strains, the object distribution will be given as

$$g(x,y) = f(\alpha x, \beta y) \tag{1}$$

where $f(x,y)$ is the distribution from the original object in the unstressed state and α and β express stress applied along the x and y directions, respectively. We assume here that the stress is applied in the elastic range of the material.

Using an appropriate optical correlator in the image plane, the following correlation function will be generated.

$$I_{gf}(x,y) = \iint f(x', y')\, g^*(x'-x, y'-y)\, dx'dy' \tag{2}$$

where the optical system used to generate I_{gf} is assumed to have a high resolving power so that no image degradation disturbs the correlation value.

If the two functions are normalized in such a manner that $<|f|^2> = <|g|^2>$ where $< >$ means averaging by the arguments, we know

$$I_{ff}(0,0) \geq I_{fg}(0,0) \tag{3}$$

Having appropriate optics in the correlator, changing the magnification of the function g for the x and y directions, and maximizing the output correlation function, we know that the image of the function g becomes identical to f because when

$$g\left(\frac{x}{m_x}, \frac{y}{m_y}\right) = f(x,y) \tag{4}$$

where $\alpha = m_x$ and $\beta = m_y$, I_{fg} is maximized. Therefore, knowing the quantities m_x and m_y, we can obtain the strains along both the x and y axis from the following relation

$$\begin{aligned} \alpha &= 1 + \varepsilon_{xx} \\ \beta &= 1 + \varepsilon_{yy} \end{aligned} \tag{5}$$

However, since it is generally very difficult to measure m_x and m_y accurately, the setup shown in Fig. 1 has been suggested. The object specimen is illuminated one dimensionally. First a hologram is produced for an unstrained object using a point source which is located in the same plane as the object (Fourier transform hologram). Then the object is stressed. The hologram of the unstressed object is precisely repositioned and is illuminated by a wavefront from the object being stressed. The field behind the holographic plane propagating in the direction of the original reference beam is focused by a spherical lens at an appropriate plane. The field at the focal point (0,0), which corresponds to the image position of the reference point source, is

$$I_{gf} = \exp\left[ik(L/2)\,(\mu^2 + \nu^2)\right] \int f^*(x,y)\, g(x,y)\, dx\, dy \tag{6}$$

where $k = 2\pi/\lambda$; λ is the wavelength, and L is the distance from the lens to the observation plane (e.g., $1/L + 1/D = 1/F$ where D is the distance between the object and the hologram, and F is the focal length). (μ,ν) is a transverse coordinate of the reference point. Since the object is illuminated by a line source from the cylindrical lens, the two-dimensional object distributions

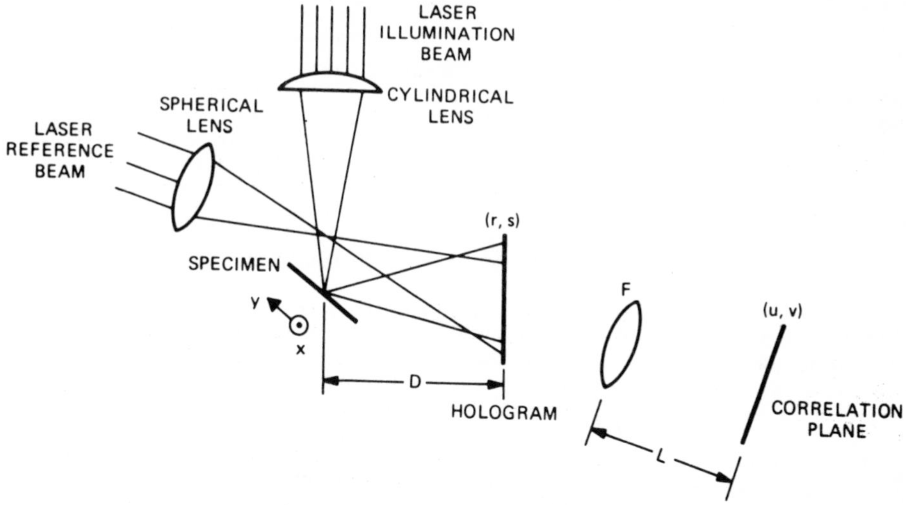

Fig. 1 Holographic correlation system to measure one-dimensional strain.

f(x,y) from the unstressed object and g(x,y) from the stressed object are replaced by one-dimensional distributions so that f and g of Eq. (6) become

$$\begin{aligned} f(x,y) &= f(x)\,\delta(y - y_0) \\ g(x,y) &= g(x)\,\delta(y - y_0) \end{aligned} \tag{7}$$

In order to change the magnification of the function g, the distance D has been changed. For the new distance $\bar{D}$, the distribution is given as

$$\bar{I}_{fg}(0,0) = \exp\left[ik\,\frac{\bar{L}}{2}\,(\mu^2 + \nu^2)\right] \int f^*(x)\; g\left(\frac{\bar{D}}{D}\,x\right) \exp\left[-ik\,\frac{x^2}{2D}\left(1 - \frac{\bar{D}}{D}\right)\right] dx \tag{8}$$

where $\bar{L}$ is the new distance as determined from $1/\bar{L} + 1/\bar{D} = 1/F$. Therefore, where $D/\bar{D}$ ($= m_x$) $= \alpha$, the output intensity will be maximized, because

$$g\left(\frac{\bar{D}}{D}\,x\right) = g(\alpha x) = f(x) \tag{9}$$

where it is assumed that we can ignore the spherical wave term by imposing the following condition on x (a length of the line illumination):

$$x^2_{max} < \lambda D/2\,|\varepsilon| \tag{10}$$

From Eq. (5) we can measure the strain ε as

$$\varepsilon = (\bar{D} - D)/D \tag{11}$$

$\bar{D}$ can be measured relatively easily as the proper spacing between the specimen and the filter. Similarly, the strain along the y direction will be measured by preparing another hologram for an object rotated 90°.

After this brief review of the principles underlying strain measurement by optical correlation, we will present two new methods for strain measurement. In both methods, the object function f (or g) is assumed to be a complicated pattern that includes high frequency components. (Such a pattern is expected from the surface of an unpolished material. Furthermore, the analysis will be limited to in-plane strain.

In the first method, beam scanning (discrete static scanning) is used in addition to holography, and the two-dimensional strain distributions will be displayed in an analog or digital fashion. In the second method, image-image correlation is used along with scanning (continuous and discrete scan). If the data obtained are analyzed with a computer, a rapid display of the complete two-dimensional strain distribution may be possible. The experimental data are also presented.

STRAIN MEASUREMENT USING A CODED HOLOGRAM

One method for using an optical correlator to measure strain in a material has been briefly reviewed in the preceding section. Here we will describe a technique using a coded hologram and beam scan (discrete scan) that results in a display of the two-dimensional strain distribution in the correlation plane. The method is based on the following two processes:

- Each part of the object (unstressed) is illuminated by a laser beam of small diameter. The reflected beam is sequentially coded[4] in a hologram along with the corresponding reference beam which is generated by beam scanning of the coding pattern.

- The stressed object is scanned (discretely) by the same small beam, and the hologram is reconstructed by the beam. The reconstructed image for the entire scan is a code pattern which is deformed by the stress of the object so that the strain distribution is displayed by a simple process (moiré method or computer).

A schematic of the system is shown in Fig. 2. Narrow beams pass through scanners to strike the test object [unstressed; f(x,y)] and the reference object [r(x,y)].

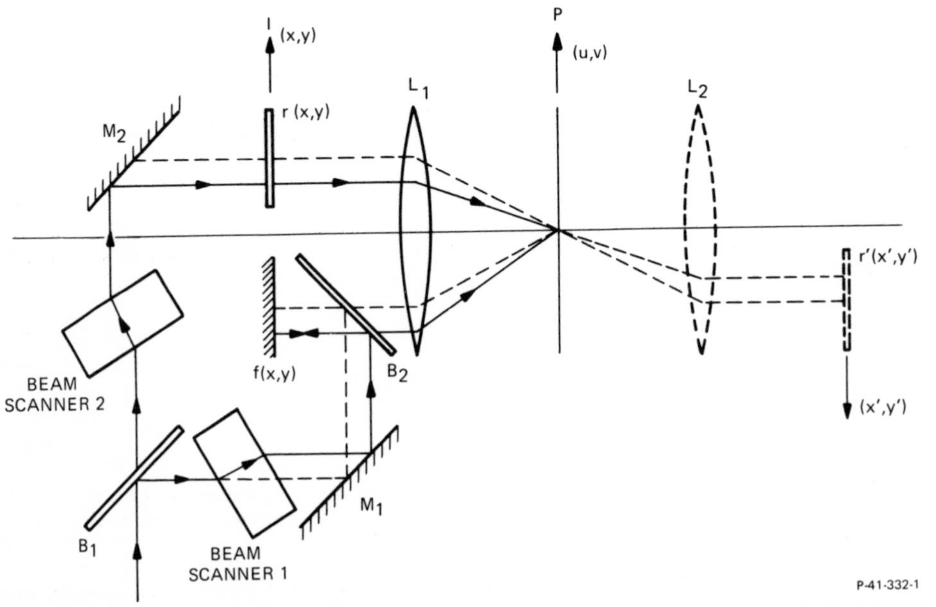

Fig. 2 Holographic strain measurement system using coded reference beam

The field in the 0 plane will be expressed as

$$f(x,y)\ t_1(x - na,\ y - mb) = f_{nm}(x - na,\ y - mb) \tag{12}$$

and

$$r(x,y)\ t_2(x - na',\ y - mb') = r_{nm}(x - na',\ y - mb')$$

where f_{nm} is the smallest distinguishable area of the distribution f(x,y) and r_{nm} is the corresponding reference wave from the distribution r(x,y). t_1 and t_2 are defined as

$$\begin{aligned} t_1(x,y) &= 1 \quad |x| < d_x \text{ and } |y| < d_y \\ &= 0 \quad |x| > d_x \text{ and } |y| > d_y \\ t_2(x,y) &= 1 \quad |x| < d'_x \text{ and } |y| < d'_y \\ &= 0 \quad |x| > d'_x \text{ and } |y| > d'_y \end{aligned} \tag{13}$$

e.g., d and d' are the beam widths and a,b a',b' are scanning intervals (sampling intervals) for the object and the reference distributions along the x and y directions. These two fields propagated through the lens are Fourier-transformed and generate an interference fringe given as

$$\begin{aligned} P_{nm} &= |F_{nm}|^2 + |R_{nm}|^2 + F^*_{nm}(\xi,\eta)\ R_{nm}(\xi,\eta)\ e^{-in(a-a')\xi-im(b-b')\eta} \\ &+ F_{nm}(\xi,\eta)\ R^*_{nm}(\xi,\eta)\ e^{in(a-a')\xi+im(b-b')\eta} \end{aligned} \tag{14}$$

where

$$\begin{aligned} F_{nm}(\xi,\eta) &= \iint f_{nm}(x,y)\ e^{ix\xi+iy\eta}\ dx\ dy \\ R_{nm}(\xi,\eta) &= \iint r_{nm}(x,y)\ e^{ix\xi+iy\eta}\ dx\ dy \end{aligned} \tag{15}$$

and $\xi = \frac{2\pi}{\lambda}\frac{\mu}{f}$ and $\eta = \frac{2\pi}{\lambda}\frac{\nu}{f}$, (f: focal length of the lens).

If all fringes for each (nm) are recorded in a hologram, the amplitude transmittance will be proportional to

$$H = \sum_n \sum_m P_{nm} \tag{16}$$

When this hologram is illuminated with the beam reflected from object f_{nm}, the reconstruction image for that part (n,m) will be given as an inverse Fourier transform of the third term of Eq. (14), e.g.,

$$\begin{aligned} i_{nnmm} &= \iint R_{nm}(\xi,\eta)\ e^{ina'\xi+imb'\eta}\ e^{-ix'\xi-iy'\eta}\ d\xi\ d\eta \\ &= r_{nm}(x' - na',\ y' - mb') \end{aligned} \tag{17}$$

On the other hand, the other part (n'm') of the image will be

$$i_{nn'mm'} = f_{nm} \otimes f^*_{n'm'} \otimes r_{n'm'} \tag{18}$$

where $\otimes$ expresses a convolution integral.

Since f_{nm} and $f_{n'm'}$ are different parts of the object, it is possible to assume that they have no mutual correlation;

$$f_{nm} \otimes f^*_{n'm'} \doteqdot 0 \tag{19}$$

Then

$$i_{nn'mm'} = 0$$

After we scan the entire object, the total reconstruction image will be then given as

$$I_{ff} = \sum_n \sum_m i_{nnmm} = \sum_n \sum_m r_{nm}(x' - na', y' - mb') = r(x', y') \tag{20}$$

which is an image of the reference source.

Based on the assumption of the preceding section, the object is now deformed to $g(x,y) = f(\alpha x, \beta y)$. When we illuminate this object by scanning of light with the aperture t_1, the field from the deformed object will be

$$g(x,y)\ t_1(x - na, y - mb) = g_{nm}(x - na, y - mb) = f_{nm}(\alpha x - na, \beta y - mb) \tag{21}$$

If we illuminate the hologram with this distribution, the reconstructed image will be

$$\begin{aligned} i'_{nnmm} &= \frac{1}{\alpha\beta}\int F^*_{nm}(\xi,\eta)\ R_{nm}(\xi,\eta)\ e^{-in(a-a')\xi-im(b-b')\eta} \\ &\quad \times F_{nm}\left(\frac{\xi}{\alpha}, \frac{\eta}{\beta}\right) e^{i\frac{na}{\alpha}\xi+i\frac{mb}{\beta}\eta} \cdot e^{-ix'\xi-iy'\eta}\ d\xi\ d\eta \\ &= r_{nm}\ [x' - n\ (a' - \varepsilon_{xx}\ a),\ y' - m(b' - \varepsilon_{yy}\ b)] \end{aligned} \tag{22}$$

where α and β are assumed to be the same as those defined in Eq. (5). Moreover, terms of an order higher than second order in the Taylor expansion of F_{nm} are neglected; $\varepsilon f^*_{nm} \otimes d^2 \dfrac{f_{nm}}{d\xi\ d\eta} \simeq 0$, because ε is a small quantity and correlation between f^* and f' decreases. Based on the assumption of Eq. (18), we know that

$$i'_{nn'mm'} = f^*_{nm} \otimes g_{n'm'} \times r_{n'm'} = 0 \tag{23}$$

Therefore, the resultant reconstructed image is

$$I_{fg} = \sum_n \sum_m i'_{nnmm} = \sum_n \sum_m r[x' - n(a' - \varepsilon_{xx}\ a),\ y' - m(b' - \varepsilon_{yy}\ b)] \tag{24}$$

From the assumption, the reference beam pattern (coding pattern) $r(x,y)$ can be an arbitrary function. We chose here $r(x,y)$ to be an assembly of delta functions (comb. function), that is

$$r(x,y) = \sum_n \sum_m \delta(x - na', y - mb') \tag{25}$$

Note that the sampling intervals a and b are longer than the beam diameter d'_x and d'_y of Eq. (13). Then from Eq. (22), the reconstructed image will be

$$r'(x',y') = \sum_n \sum_m \delta(x' - na' + n\,\varepsilon_{xx}\,a,\ y' - mb' + m\,\varepsilon_{yy}\,b) \tag{26}$$

In this manner, strain measurement for an arbitrary object f(x,y) is reduced to measuring the deviation ($n\,\varepsilon_{xx}\,a$, $m\,\varepsilon_{yy}\,b$) of the comb function. Since each data function is generated independently according to the scanning, the intensity of the image will be regarded as identical to Eq. (22). The intensity distribution of Eq. (26) can then be written in terms of its Fourier components as

$$|r'(x',y')|^2 = \sum_n \sum_m \delta(x' - na' + n\,\varepsilon_{xx}\,a,\ y' - mb' + m\,\varepsilon_{yy}\,b)$$

$$= \sum_p \sum_q \left[1 + \cos\left\{\frac{2\pi p}{a'}\left(1 + \frac{a}{a'}\,\varepsilon_{xx}\right)x' + \frac{2\pi q}{b'}\left(1 + \frac{b}{b'}\,\varepsilon_{yy}\right)y'\right\}\right] \tag{27}$$

By applying the moiré technique to Eq. (27), strain information can be obtained; superimposing a sinusoidal mask whose transmittance is given as

$$m(x',y') = 1 + \cos\left(\frac{2}{a'}\,p_o\,x' + \frac{2}{b'}\,q_o\,y'\right);\ p_o \text{ and } q_o \text{ are integers} \tag{28}$$

on the image and removing all high frequency components with an optical filter, we will have

$$|r'|^2\, m(x',y')\ \{\text{filtered}\} = 1 + \frac{1}{2}\cos\left\{\frac{2\pi a}{a'^2}\,\varepsilon_{xx}\,p_o\,x' + \frac{2\pi b}{b'^2}\,\varepsilon_{yy}\,q_o\,y'\right\} \tag{29}$$

This is nothing more than direct display of the strain distribution. It is important to note here that, because we are using a comb function as a reference function (coding function), we can alter the sensitivity of the system simply by selecting a high frequency sinusoidal mask $\left(\frac{2\pi}{a'}\,p_o,\ \frac{2\pi}{b'}\,q_o\right)$.

The accuracy of this system may therefore be expected to be at least the same as that of the method described in the introduction to this paper (e.g., in principle, 10 ppm or better). The pattern resulting from Eq. (27) may be processed in many ways; computer processing with a vidicon scan of the distribution may be a possibility.

IMAGE-IMAGE CORRELATION FOR 2-D STRAIN MEASUREMENT

Similar problems dealt with in the previous section will be approached with more direct correlation measurement. Optical image-image correlation has been suggested by Kretzmer[5] and developed for many purposes. In photogrammetry,[6] the technique is most actively applied to one-dimensional problems. We will apply this same technique to 2-D strain measurement problem using the setup shown in Fig. 3. In this image-image correlation technique, it may be more convenient to prepare a photographic transparency of the object examined [f(x,y) and g(x,y)] by a processing procedure. This limits the sensitivity of the system, but otherwise there is no way to store the original information.

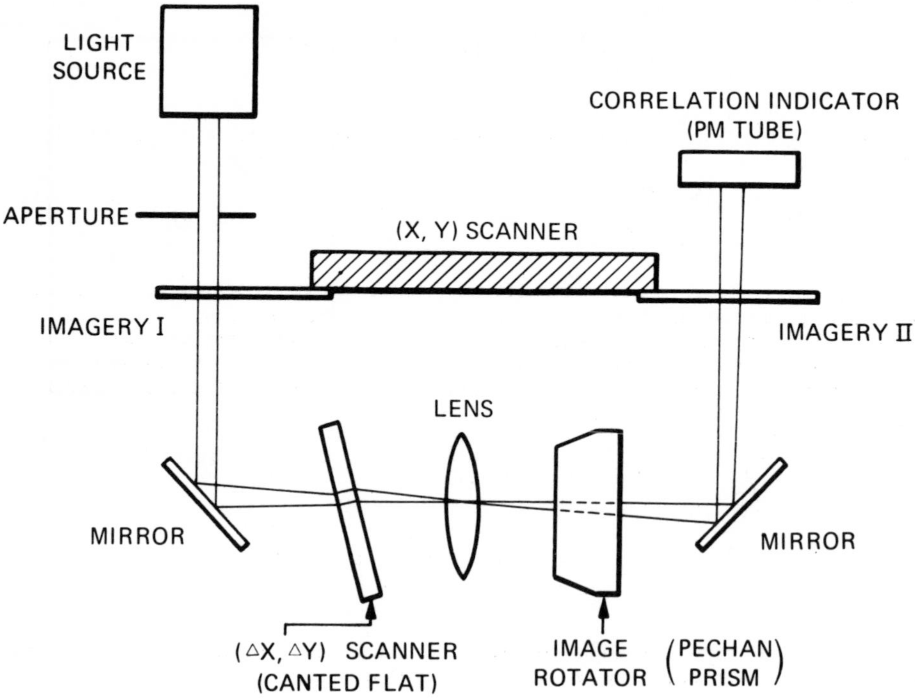

Fig. 3 Image-image correlation to measure two-dimensional strain distribution

In Fig. 3, a laser beam passing through an appropriate aperture t_1 illuminates the photographic plate on which the original object information f(x,y) is recorded.

The field behind the photograph will be

$$f_{nm}\ (x - na,\ y - mb) \tag{30}$$

As in Eq. (12), the center of the function t_1 is at (na, mb). The field will be propagated to another photographic plate (imagery) by the two mirrors.

The second photographic plate records the stressed object information [g(x,y)]. The image of f_{nm} is formed on this plate by the lens. Therefore, the intensity detected by the PM tube will be proportional to

$$I_{fg} = \iint f_{nm}(x,y)\ g_{nm}(x,y)\ dx\ dy \tag{31}$$

If g(x,y) = f(x,y), and both functions are positioned in such a way that the beam illuminates the identical portions, the above function will be maximized and the signal will be I_{ff} for all points (n,m) which are altered by a large (x,y) scanner. However, the function g is a stressed pattern as given in Eq. (1). In order to maximize the output intensity, we have to shift the image of f_{nm} in the plane of the secondary plate (Imagery II). This is performed by an inserted glass plate (Δx, Δy) scanner.

If the thickness of the parallel glass plate (reflective index n) is d, the tiltness of the plate is θ_o, and furthermore, if the tilted plate is rotated along the optical axis (as shown in Fig. 4), the effective axis will be

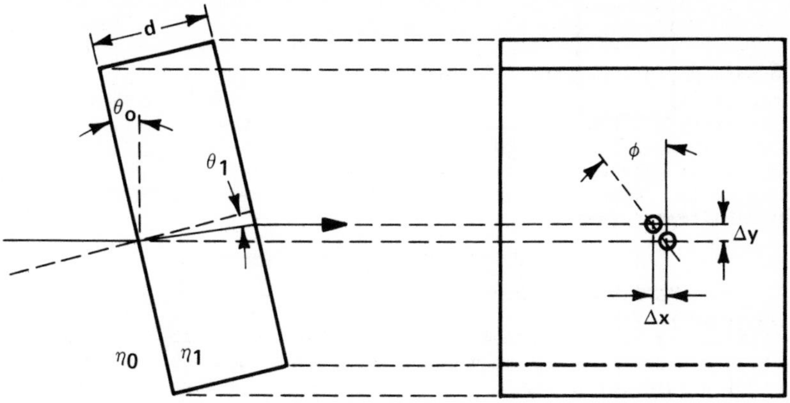

Fig. 4 Glass plate used in the system shown in Figure 3

shifted in the ϕ direction from the y axis by an amount of $|\Delta x|^2 + |\Delta y|^2$ given as

$$|\Delta x|^2 + |\Delta y|^2 = \frac{d \sin (\theta_o - \theta_1)}{\cos \theta_1}$$
$$\tan \phi = \frac{\Delta y}{\Delta x} \tag{32}$$

where θ_1 is given by

$$\sin \theta_o = n_1 \sin \theta_1 \tag{33}$$

Then Eq. (31) will be

$$I_{fg} = \iint f_{nm} (x - na - \Delta x_{nm}, y - mb - \Delta y_{nm}) \times f_{nm} (\alpha x - na, \beta y - mb) \, dx \, dy \tag{34}$$

Using the same considerations required to deduce Eq. (24), we can see from Eq. (34) that I_{fg} will be maximized when

$$\Delta x_{nm} = \varepsilon_{xx} x$$
$$\Delta y_{nm} = \varepsilon_{yy} y \tag{35}$$

where α, β, ε_{xx},and ε_{yy} are the same as that given in Eq. (5).

For every (na, mb) point, if Δx_n and Δy_m (which make I_{fg} maximum) are obtained by measuring ϕ and θ_o [Eq. (32) and (33)], the two-dimensional strain distribution will be calculated by taking a derivative of the Δx_n and Δy_m distributions, e.g.,

$$\varepsilon_{xx}(na,mb) = \frac{\Delta x_{n+1,m} - \Delta x_{n,m}}{a}$$
$$\varepsilon_{yy}(na,mb) = \frac{\Delta y_{nm+1} - \Delta y_{nm}}{b} \tag{36}$$

If in the above discussions we are interested in only linear strain [given in Eq. (5)], Eq. (36) will give sufficient information. However, if the object stressed is inhomogeneous and has shear strain (rotation component ε_{xy}, ε_{yx}), we need another component to measure it. This normally requires additional complexity in the measuring process. However, in the system shown in Fig. 3, shear strain can be measured relatively easily using the image rotator (Pechan prism) shown in the figure. In this case, the output I_{fg} of the system is maximized not only by Δx and Δy but also by rotating the input image f_{nm} by a small angle $\Delta\phi$. Knowing accurately Δx, Δy, and $\Delta\phi$, we will be able to plot the in-plane strain distribution completely.

EXPERIMENTAL

A preliminary experiment intended to show the feasibility of the correlation technique has been performed using image-image correlation. The latter concept has been developed into an established instrument for aerographic application. For strain measurement, such an instrument designed for photogrammetry was used (Fig. 5). The principle of the instrument is similar to that explained in the preceding section (Fig. 3). The instrument is computerized so that all photogrammetric information is automatically processed and displayed. Although it is possible to modify the instrument for automated strain measurement, we measured the strain distribution manually in our preliminary experiments. The specimen consisted of a piece of unprocessed photographic film, cut into a pincushion shape, and sprayed with black paint in order to make a complicated pattern for f(x,y). Both ends of the specimen are tightened with a mechanical clamp which can stretch the specimen along one direction. Fig. 6 shows the specimen in the stressed and unstressed states. The stressed specimen has been completely stretched by the clamp. The total length of the specimen (the distance from the right edge to the left edge of the picture) is 7 cm and the distance of the shortest portion is 2.5 cm.

The photographic negatives from the stressed and unstressed specimens Δx and Δy [explained in Eq. (37)] were measured over the entire specimen; sampling intervals [a and b in Eq. (30)] are 3 mm for both directions.

After numerical processing using Eq. (36), the strain distribution has been plotted in Fig. 7. The contour map of the strain along the direction stressed is reasonable. The asymmetry observed in the contour map is probably caused by geometrical imperfections in the pincushion shape. The accuracy in

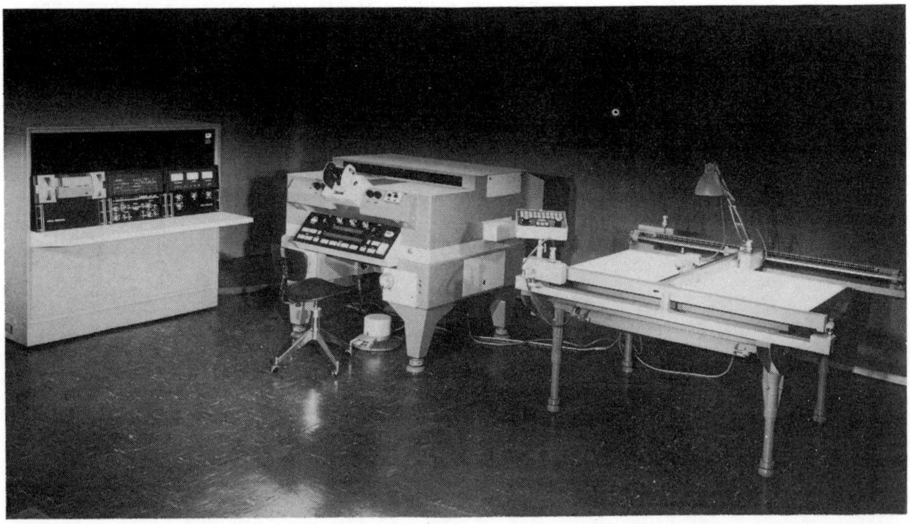

Fig. 5 Photographs of automated photogrammetric instrument

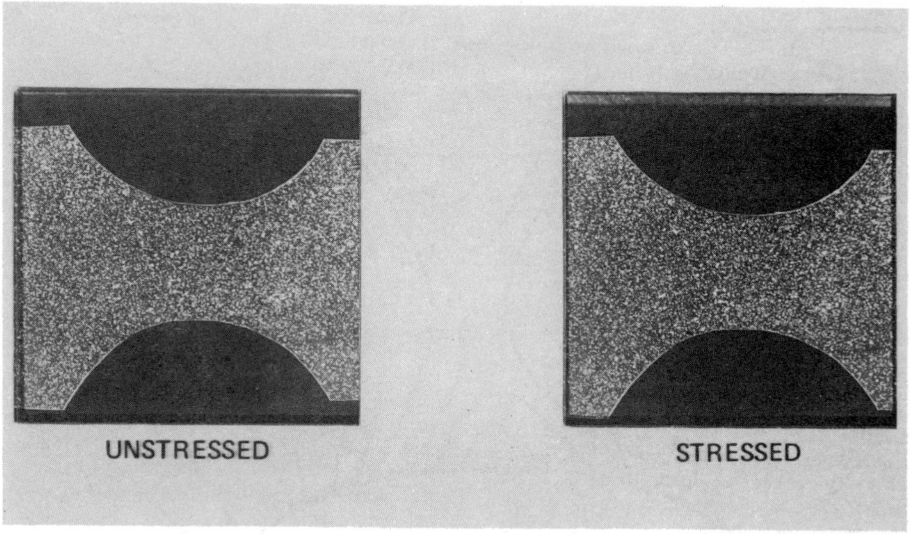

Fig. 6 Pictures of specimen, right, stressed and left unstressed

this measurement is quite rough, e.g., minimum strain is 10 μ/mm. However, the instrument can measure even a few micrometers in length. Therefore, if we have, for example, a photographic system[7] which has a resolution of 80 line/mm over 21 cm (9") format, we can expect approximately 4×10^{-4} strain/mm on that format. Furthermore, with better quality lenses we will be able to increase the sensitivity.

SUMMARY

Two correlation methods for in-plane strain analysis have been suggested. In the first method, a holographic matched filter was used to generate a coded image. The distribution of the unstressed object was divided into the smallest independently distinguishable segment, and a matched filter for each segment was produced with a corresponding reference wave (coded wave). When the hologram is sequentially illuminated by each segment of the stressed object, the reconstructed coded pattern (two-dimensional comb functions were used) appears in a form modulated by the stress. Since the comb function consists of sinusoidal patterns of various frequencies superposed, the deviation of the comb function can be easily measured. That is, we can use the moiré method of preparing a sinusoidal mask whose frequency corresponds to one of the higher frequency components of the comb function to pick up the deviation. In this case, the sensitivity of the deviation (strain) display is determined by the frequency of the sinusoidal pattern selected and the size of the small segments of the object. Computer analysis of the deviated comb function with appropriate vidicon scan of the displayed pattern may be possible. The sensitivity of this system depends upon the detail of the object function, but we may expect to detect 10 ppm strain in a normal metal surface using accurately aligned equipment.

Our second method uses straightforward image-image correlation to measure the displacements within the stressed object. Since this technique is well established for the photogrammetric purpose, data analysis and display can be easily automated for strain measurement. The drawback of this technique is the use of photographic processing which limits the sensitivity. Therefore, the maximum sensitivity we can expect is about the same as that of the conventional moiré method, but lends itself more easily to automated processing. The preliminary experimental data show reasonable results regarding the usefulness of the method for strain measurement applications.

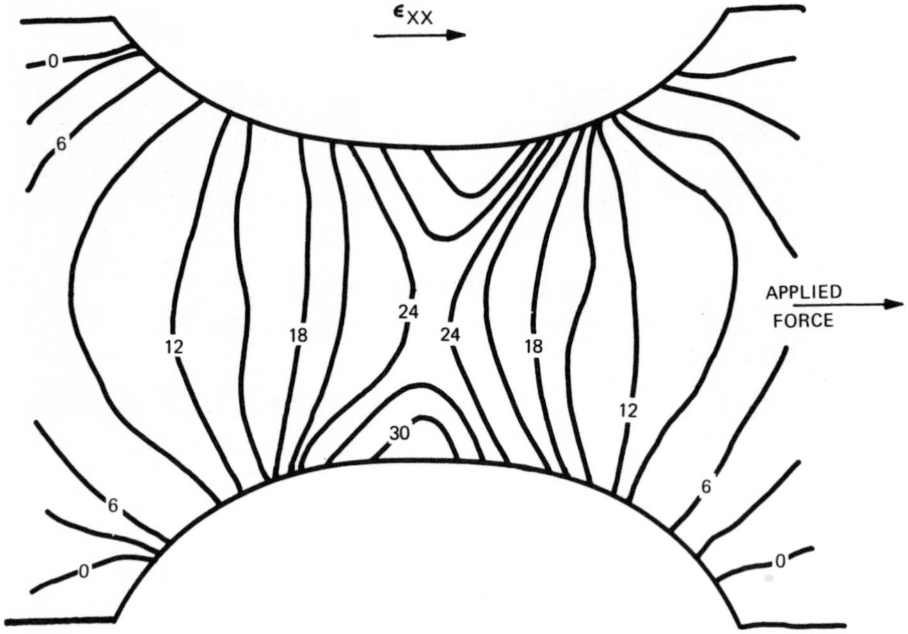

Fig. 7 Experimental results; strain distribution; number indicated is 1/10 (%) strain

ACKNOWLEDGMENTS

The authors would like to thank Drs. P. N. Keating and R. R. Gupta for their useful discussions and Mrs. S. Benigna for her help in preparing the manuscript.

REFERENCES

1 J. E. Sollid, Applied Optics, Vol. 8, 1969, p. 1587.

2 R. Weller and B. M. Shepard, Proceedings of SESA, Vol. 1, 1948, p. 35.

3 E. Marom and R. K. Mueller, Journal of the Optical Society of America, Vol. 59, No. 11, 1969, p. 1517a and E. Marom, Applied Optics, Vol. 9, No. 6, 1970, p. 1385.

4 E. N. Leith, et al., Laser Focus, Vol. 1, 1965, p. 15.

5 E. R. Kretzmer, Bell System Technical Journal, Vol. 31, 1952, p. 751.

6 For example, America Society of Photogrammetry: Manual of Photogrammetry, 3rd ed., Vol. 1, Washington, D.C., 1966.

7 Ibid., Chapter III.

MOIRÉ ANALYSIS OF DISPLACEMENT AND STRAIN FIELDS

By

CESAR A. SCIAMMARELLA

Professor, Polytechnic Institute of Brooklyn

ABSTRACT

The moiré method provides a means for the direct determination of displacement and strain fields in two and three dimensional surfaces. This paper is primarily written as a unified presentation of the moiré method. Basic fundamentals necessary to comprehend the subject are reviewed and expanded to give a clear understanding and a working knowledge of the entire area from a common point of view.

The broad scope of the material introduced in this paper should give to the reader a good basis to grasp most of the present state of the art developments in the area of moiré. It is the hope of the author that upon reading this paper, readers will be able to see some of the possible applications of the moiré method to their fields of endeavor.

In view of the length of the material already included in the paper, it has not been possible to introduce applications of the moiré method. At this point it is enough to say that the moiré method has found many applications in problems of engineering interest, such as plasticity, thermal stresses, viscoelastic materials, composites, pressure vessels, plates and shells.

NOMENCLATURE

$a(x, y)$ = amplitude part of the transmission function.

$\underset{\sim}{d}$ = displacement vector.

E = amplitude of light vector. Subscripts indicate diffraction order.

$\overset{r-n}{\underset{n}{E}}$ = $E_n \, E_{r-n}$.

$\underset{\sim}{E}$ = light vector complex amplitude. Subscripts indicate diffraction order. Double subscripts indicate order sequence.

$\underset{\sim}{F}(x, y)$ = transmission function.

f = focal distance of lens.

h_p = weight of filtering function

$(h_p)_q$ = weight of quadrature filtering function.

i = angle defining incident beam with respect to the normal to the grating.

$I(x)$ = light intensity at a point of coordinate x in image plane.

I_o = background light intensity in image plane.

I_n = light intensity amplitude of image, nth harmonic.

$\tilde{I}_k$ = filtered version of I(x).

$\bar{I}(x)$ = Fourier transform of I(x).

$K(\nu_x, \nu_y)$ = pupil function of the image-forming system.

$\bar{K}(\nu_x, \nu_y)$ = Fourier transform of $K(\nu_x, \nu_y)$.

$L(\nu_x, \nu_y)$ = Frequency-response function of the image-forming system.

$\bar{L}(\nu_x, \nu_y)$ = Fourier transform of $L(\nu_x, \nu_y)$.

m = magnification of lens system

p = grid pitch.

$p(x)$ = local value of the grid pitch.

u, v, w = displacements of points of model parallel to x, y, z coordinate axes, respectively.

$U_1(\nu_x, \nu_y)$,
$U_o(\nu_x, \nu_y)$ = light complex amplitude vectors of image and object. Bar quantities indicate Fourier transforms.

t = gap between gratings.

$T(x, y)$ = transmittance function

$\alpha(x, y)$ = phase part of the transmission function.

β_n = angle of the nth order diffracted wave front with the normal to the grating.

ω = angular frequency.

δ = fringe spacing

$\overline{\Delta x}$ = shear introduced in the x direction equal, to 2 Δx.

Δy = shear introduced in the y direction.

$\overline{\Delta y}$ = shear introduced in the y direction, equal to 2 Δx.

ϵ = strain.

$\theta(x)$ = total angle rotated by the vector representing the light complex amplitude from the origin of coordinates.

γ = slope of density versus logarithm of exposure curve.

θ_r = angle defining the emerging beam with respect to the normal to the grating.

θ_n = angle defining diffracted beam with respect to the normal to the grating.

θ_i' = angle defining incident beam with respect to principal plane π_1.

θ_i'' = angle defining incident beam with respect to secondary plane π_2.

θ_n' = angle defining diffracted beam of order n with respect to principal plane π_1.

θ_n'' = angle defining diffracted beam of order n with respect to secondary plane π_2.

$\theta_{n'}$ = angle defining diffracted beam of order n with respect to the normal to the deformed grating.

λ = wavelength of light.

ν = spatial frequency

π_1 = principal plane (plane perpendicular to plane of grid and perpendicular to grid lines).

π_2 = secondary plane (plane perpendicular to plane of grid and parallel to grid lines).

π_3 = grating plane.

ϕ = phase of the light vector. Subscript indicates diffraction order.

$\phi_{k\ell}$ = phase of the light vector corresponding to the sequence k, ℓ.

$\overline{\Phi}_s$ = phase constants depending on characteristics of grooves of grating for the sth order.

ϕ_n^{r-n} = $\phi_n + \phi_{r-n}$.

$\overline{\psi}(x)$ = modulating function

GRATINGS

In communication theory periodic signals play a very important role. For example, sinusoidally varying functions are used extensively as carriers. Messages can be imposed on a carrier by two basic processes, amplitude modulation or frequency modulation. Gratings play a similar role in optics and both variations of amplitude and frequency can be imposed on them.

For the analysis of optical data it is necessary to consider how a desired signal can be placed in a wavefront. Let us consider a plane wavefront

$$\underset{\sim}{E}(z) = E\ e^{i\phi} \tag{1}$$

We can modify the amplitude E in equation (1), we can produce changes in the phase of the vector, or we can modify the amplitude and phase.

Let us assume that we have a plane wavefront impinging on a film or transparency. Let $\underset{\sim}{E}_i(x, y)$ be the complex amplitude function describing the incident wavefront, and $\underset{\sim}{E}_o(x, y)$ the emerging wavefront; the transmission function of the film is expressed by

$$\underset{\sim}{F}(x, y) = \frac{\underset{\sim}{E}_o(x, y)}{\underset{\sim}{E}_i(x, y)} = a(x, y)\, e^{i\alpha(x, y)} \tag{2}$$

where

$$a(x, y) = \frac{E_o(x, y)}{E_i(x, y)} \tag{3a}$$

and

$$\alpha(x, y) = \phi_o(x, y) - \phi_i(x, y) \tag{3b}$$

Since the characteristic of physical photodetectors (e.g. human eye, film, photocell) is such that they can only sense intensity of light and they cannot sense amplitude directly, another function representing the transmission properties of films must be introduced. The transmission characteristics of a film expressed in terms of intensities is defined as transmittance. If the intensity of the incident light is $I_i(x, y)$ and the intensity of the light after passing through the film is $I_o(x, y)$, the transmittance is defined as

$$T(x, y) = \frac{I_o(x, y)}{I_i(x, y)} \tag{4}$$

The transmission function and the transmittance are related by

$$T(x, y) = \underset{\sim}{F}^*(x, y) \cdot \underset{\sim}{F}(x, y) = a^2(x, y) \tag{5}$$

where the symbol * indicates the complex conjugate of the quantity.

A grid may be defined as an optical element that produces on an incident wave, periodic variations of amplitude or phase, or both. The grating will be mathematically characterized by its transmission function. If the grating alters the amplitude of the incident wave, it is called an amplitude grating and its transmission function is real. If the phase is changed the grating is called a phase grating and its transmission function is imaginary. If both the phase and amplitude are affected, the transmission function is complex.

We will consider sinusoidal gratings, having in mind that any other type of grating can be decomposed into a sum of sinusoidal gratings by application of the Fourier theorem.

The transmission function of an amplitude sinusoidal grating is of the form

$$F_1(x) = a + \frac{a}{2} \cos \frac{2\pi x}{p} \tag{6}$$

where p is the pitch of the grating, and $\frac{1}{p}$ is called the fundamental spatial frequency of the grating. Since the cosine function has negative values on alternate half cycles, and since it is impossible to have negative values of the light amplitude vector, a bias term a, has been introduced in equation (6).

At this point, it is convenient to recall an important property of lenses. Let us consider the optical set-up of Fig. 1. We have a lens and its front and back focal planes are located at the focal distance f with respect to the principal plane of the lens. The transmission of light through the object plane can be expressed by the transmission function given by equation (2). The object plane is illuminated by collimated, coherent, monochromatic light represented by the plane wave front given by equation (1). The light emerging from the object plane will be given by the equation

$$\underset{\sim}{E}_o(x, y) = F(x, y)\, E\, e^{i\phi(x, y)} =$$

$$E\, a(x, y)\, e^{i[\phi(x, y) + \alpha(x, y)]} \tag{7}$$

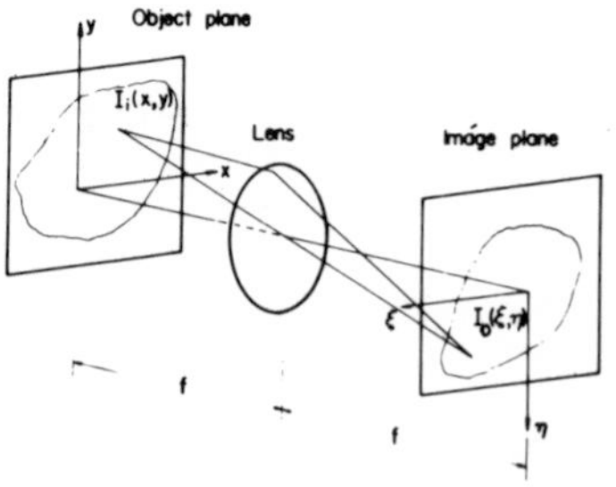

Fig. 1. Fourier transforming property of lenses.

The complex amplitudes on the front and the back focal planes are related by the equation [1]†

$$\underset{\sim}{E}_o(\xi, \eta) = \int_A \underset{\sim}{E}_o(x, y)\, e^{-\frac{i 2\pi}{\lambda}\left[\frac{\xi x}{f} + \frac{\eta y}{f}\right]}\, dxdy \tag{8}$$

† Bracket, [], indicates reference at the end of this paper.

This equation can be interpreted by the statement: the complex amplitude in the back focal plane is given by the Fourier transform of the transmission function in the front focal plane. The intensity received in the back focal plane is given by

$$I(x, y) = \underset{\sim}{E}_o^* \cdot \underset{\sim}{E}_o \tag{9}$$

Since the only possible outputs of optical systems are in the form of energy detectors (eyes, photocell, films) only the square of the amplitudes of the transform will be detected. If we put in the object plane an amplitude sinusoidal grating, in the back focal plane we will observe three dots, (Fig. 2), the central dot corresponds to the bias term, and the lateral dots correspond to the +1 and -1 diffraction orders. If the grating is not a sinusoidal grating but a grating with a transmission function as shown in Fig. 3, in the back focal plane we will observe a large number of dots. These dots combined in pairs of the same order together with the bias term will produce the successive harmonic that enter in the Fourier expansion of the transmission function.

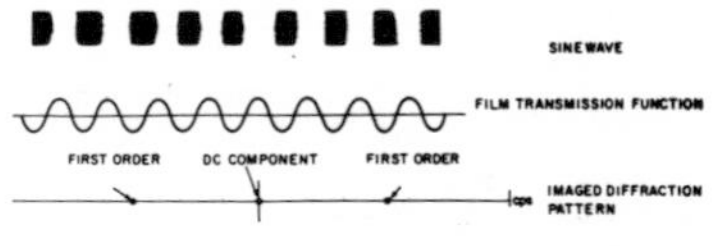

Fig. 2. Optically obtained Fourier spectrum of a sinusoidal grating.

We have considered a sinusoidal grating in only one direction. Let us suppose that we have a transmission function corresponding to two sinusoidal gratings in orthogonal direction

$$F(x, y) = a + \frac{a}{2} \cos \frac{2\pi x}{p} \cos \frac{2\pi y}{p} \tag{10}$$

The sinusoidal grating in the y direction produces a diffraction pattern in the x direction, the sinusoidal grating in the x direction produces a diffraction pattern in the y direction. If we have a sinusoidal grating with spatial orientation at 30 deg with respect to the vertical, Fig. 4, the diffraction pattern will appear at 30 deg from the vertical.

If in place of having simply sinusoidal gratings, we have more complex gratings, the diffraction pattern will be composed of arrays of dots.

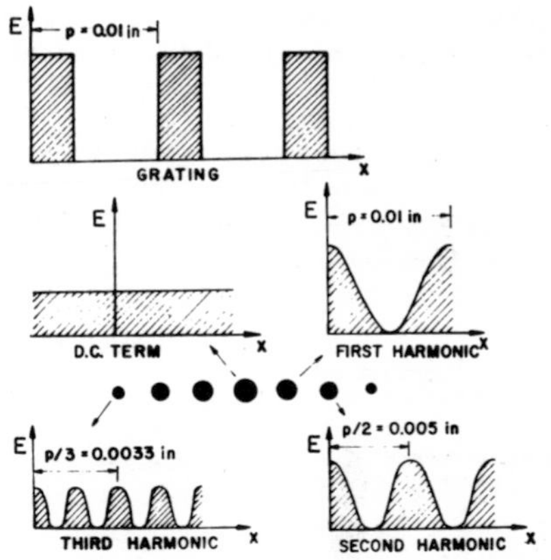

Fig. 3. Fourier spectrum of an amplitude grating.

Let us consider a grating contained in the x, y plane of the coordinate system of Fig. 5. A plane wavefront of light of wave length λ and unit amplitude incident normally to the grating, as it passes through the grating, is split into the different diffraction orders. The angles of the diffraction orders with respect to the grating normal are given by the equation

$$\sin \theta_n = \frac{n\lambda}{p} \tag{11}$$

The wavefronts emerging from the grating can be represented by the equation

$$\underset{\sim}{E}(x, z) = E_o e^{\frac{2\pi iz}{\lambda}} + \sum_{j=1}^{j=n} E_j e^{2\pi i \frac{z \cos \theta_j + x \sin \theta_j}{\lambda}} + \sum_{j=1}^{j=n} E_j e^{2\pi i \frac{z \cos \theta_j - x \sin \theta_j}{\lambda}} \tag{12}$$

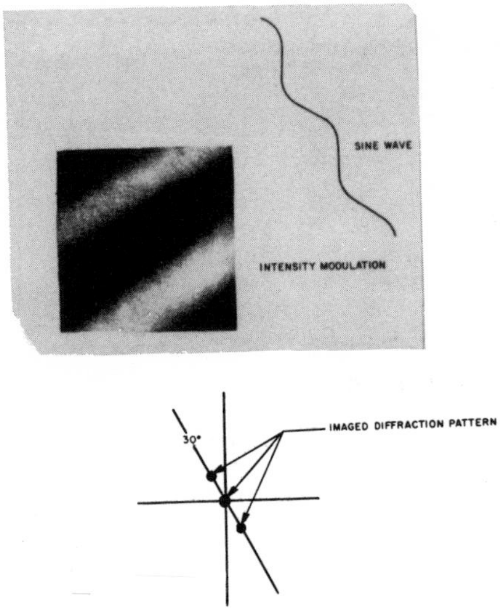

Fig. 4. Fourier spectrum of a sinusoidal grating oriented at 30 deg with respect to the vertical.

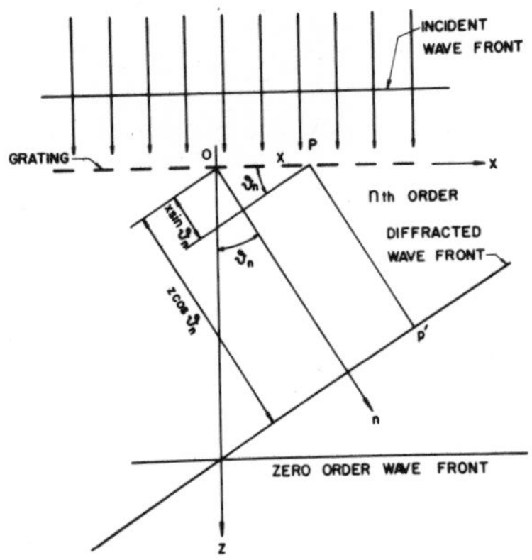

Fig. 5. Wave fronts produced by a diffraction grating and system of coordinates.

where the first term corresponds to the zero-order wave front, the second and third terms correspond to the negative and the positive diffraction orders. The arguments of the exponential function are the phases of the wave fronts with respect to the plane $z = 0$.

We have seen how a lens acts as a spectrum analyzer, producing in its back focal plane the spectrum of the transmission function of a grating located in its front focal plane. If the diffraction spectrum in the back focal plane of lens I, Fig. 6, is used as an object in the front focal plane of lens II, the back

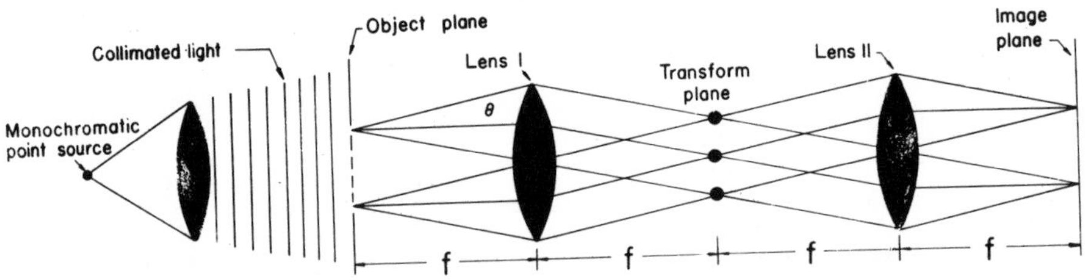

Fig. 6. Optical arrangement for optical filtering.

focal plane of lens II will contain an image of the grating. We have produced a transform of a transform, which gives the original transmission function. It is easy to see that in the front focal plane of lens II we can stop some frequencies, and the resulting image will lack these particular components. This process is called optical filtering. By means of the optical filtering process we can control the number of terms of equation (12) that will contribute to the formation of the image.

We can allow to pass only the bias background term and one frequency, in this case we will get a sinusoidal grating of the corresponding frequency. If we have two orthogonal gratings we can eliminate one of the two systems of lines (Fig. 7a, Fig. 7b) or we can get (Fig. 7c) a grating of 45 deg by allowing to pass the orders along the 45 deg diagonal. By selecting other diagonal lines we can produce gratings in many intermediate directions between the x and the y directions.

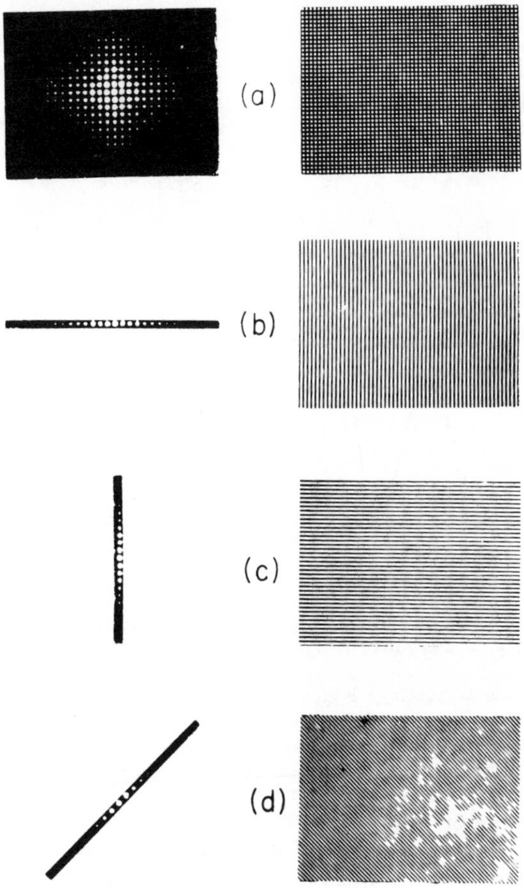

Fig. 7. Photograph of a grating and its spectrum. (a) Cross-grating and spectrum; (b) vertical lines and spectrum; (c) horizontal lines and spectrum; (d) lines at 45 deg and spectrum.

Gratings as Carriers of Displacement Information

We engrave on the surface of a model a grating, the grating is acting in this case as a carrier of information. The information sought is the displacement of the points of the surface of the model. At this point to simplify our analysis we assume that the grating is sinusoidal. Consequently the transmission function is given by equation (6).

Now suppose we deform the model by application of a load, equation (6) becomes

$$F_2(x) = a + \frac{a}{2} \cos \frac{2\pi x}{p(x)} \tag{13}$$

The carrier has been modulated by the deformation introduced by the load. The argument of the cosine term in equation (13) can be written as

$$\theta_2(x) = \frac{2\pi x}{p(x)} = 2\pi \left[\frac{x}{p} + \bar{\psi}(x) \right] \tag{14}$$

where $\bar{\psi}(x)$ is called the modulating function. In Fig. 8a we have represented

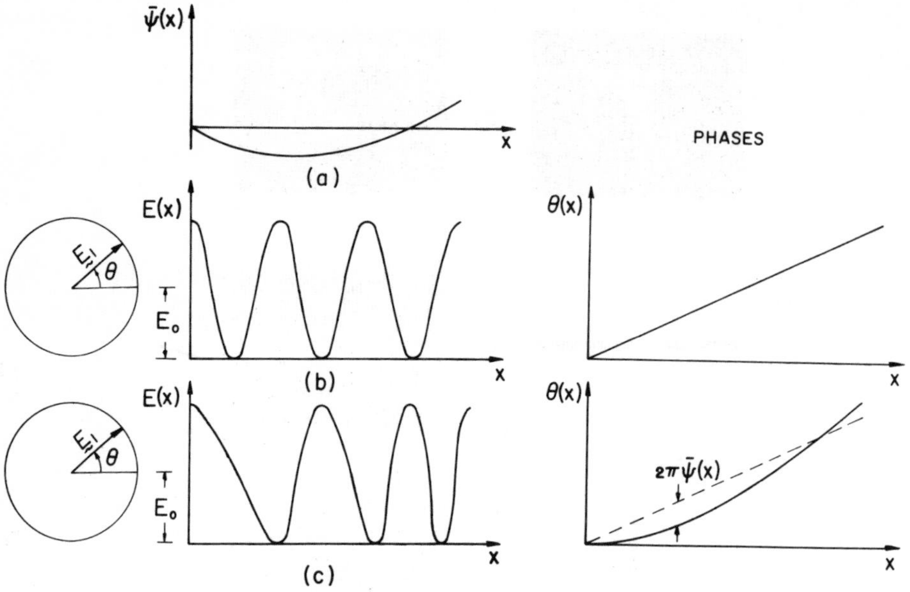

Fig. 8. Vectorial representation of a carrier. (a) modulating function; (b) undeformed carrier; (c) deformed carrier.

an assumed modulating function, Fig. 8b shows the carrier and Fig. 8c shows the modulated carrier. The vectorial representation of Fig. 8b shows the vector $\underset{\sim}{E}_1$ that rotates with constant frequency $\nu = \frac{1}{p}$ and generates the carrier. At the right of Fig. 8b the plot of the phases of the vector $\underset{\sim}{E}_1$ is given. The phase of the vector $\underset{\sim}{E}_1$ at the point of coordinate x is defined as the total angle rotated by the vector from the origin of coordinates up to the point of coordinate x. The plot at the right of Fig. 8c gives the plot of the phases of the vector that generates the modulated carrier. The phases of the modulated carrier vector are obtained by adding to the phases of the unmodulated carrier the modulating function $\bar{\psi}(x)$ as indicated by equation (14). The vector $\underset{\sim}{E}_1$ will have a changing angular velocity

$$\omega(x) = \frac{d\theta(x)}{dx} = 2\pi \left[\frac{1}{p} + \frac{d\bar{\psi}(x)}{dx} \right] \tag{15}$$

The instantaneous frequency of the phase modulated signal can be defined as

$$\frac{1}{p(x)} = \nu(x) = \frac{\omega(x)}{2\pi} = \frac{1}{p} + \frac{d\bar{\psi}(x)}{dx} \tag{16}$$

From (16)

$$\nu(x) - \nu = \frac{1}{p_{(x)}} - \frac{1}{p} = \frac{d\bar{\psi}(x)}{dx} \tag{17}$$

We need now to relate the above quantities to the applied deformation.

Let us consider Fig. 9 the point P of coordinate x_o in the undeformed condition, after deformation it will have the coordinate x. The phase vector corresponding to the amplitude of the light at the point P in the undeformed position is

$$\theta_o(x) = 2\pi \frac{x_o}{p} \tag{18}$$

Upon deformation the point P coincides with a point P_1 in the undeformed condition. The phase corresponding to P_1 is

$$\theta_1(x) = 2\pi \frac{x}{p} \quad (19)$$

The difference of the two phases is

$$\theta_1(x) - \theta_o(x) = \frac{2\pi}{p}[x - x_o] \quad (20)$$

and since by definition

$$u = x - x_o \quad (21)$$

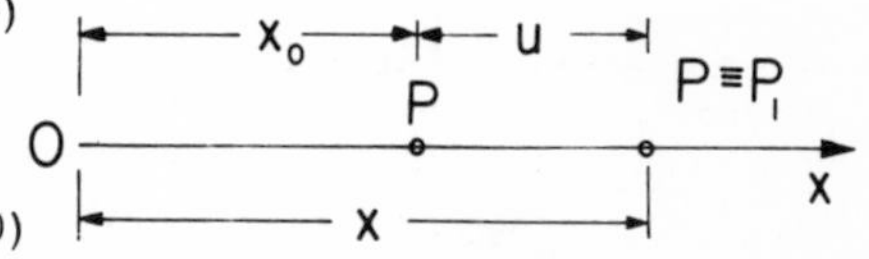

Fig. 9. Deformed and undeformed gratings.

is the displacement of the point P in the x direction

$$\theta_1(x) - \theta_o(x) = \frac{2\pi}{p} u \quad (22)$$

but in view of the fact that the grating is printed on the model

$$\theta_2(x) = \theta_o(x) = 2\pi \frac{x_o}{p} = 2\pi \frac{x}{p(x)} \quad (23)$$

since both the coordinate axis and the grating are deformed. Consequently

$$u = \frac{p}{2\pi} [\ \theta_1(x) - \theta_2(x)\ ] = p\,\overline{\psi}(x) \quad (24)$$

we can see also that according to (17) and (24)

$$\frac{du}{dx} = p\left[\frac{1}{p(x)} - \frac{1}{p}\right] = p\,(\nu(x) - \nu) = p\,\frac{d\overline{\psi}(x)}{dx} \quad (25)$$

for small deformations

$$\epsilon_x = p\,(\nu(x) - \nu) = p\,\frac{d\,\overline{\psi}(x)}{dx} \quad (26)$$

The changes of the frequencies are directly related to the strains of the model.
Our problem is to create means of detection of the information of interest to us, the displacements and their derivatives. One possible means of detection is to introduce in front of the model grating a second grating, called the reference grating.

THE MOIRÉ METHOD

In the moiré method, we are concerned with the formation of the image of two superposed gratings by an optical system - eye, camera, lens, lens system. For this purpose we can utilize the theory of imaging of extended objects by an optical system [1]. Schematically, the optical system utilized in the observation of moiré fringes consists of two gratings in the object plane, a lens, and a detector at the image plane. We can illuminate the object plane with a collimated monochromatic coherent light or we illuminate the object plane with noncoherent light.

The application of the Fourier transform to optics (see page 483 Ref. [1]) shows that an optical system behaves like a filter which allows the passage of certain spatial frequencies and rejects others.

In the case of coherent illumination, if we call $\overline{U}_1(\nu_x, \nu_y)$ the Fourier transform of the image light complex amplitude vectors, where ν_x and ν_y are spatial frequencies; $\overline{U}_o(\nu_x, \nu_y)$ the Fourier transform of the object light complex amplitude vector and $K(\nu_x, \nu_y)$ the frequency response function of the lens, or pupil function

$$\overline{U}_1(\nu_x, \nu_y) = \overline{U}_o(\nu_x, \nu_y)\,\overline{K}(\nu_x, \nu_y) \tag{27}$$

From equation (27) it follows that each frequency component of the image depends only on the corresponding component of the object, and that the ratio of these components is $\overline{K}$. If we consider a perfect lens, Fig. 10, $\overline{K}(\nu_x, \nu_y) = 1$, if $\nu_x^2 + \nu_y^2 < \nu_{max}^2$, where ν_{max} is the maximum spatial frequency that the lens system will allow to pass. The image transmission function will not be identical to the object transmission function, it will lack certain frequencies.

If the illumination is non-coherent, a relationship similar to equation (27) applies to the light intensity distribution.

Calling $\overline{I}_1(\nu_x, \nu_y)$ the Fourier transform of the image intensity, $\overline{I}_o(\nu_x, \nu_y)$ the Fourier transform of the object intensity, and $\overline{L}(\nu_x, \nu_y)$ the response function of the lens

$$\overline{I}_1(\nu_x, \nu_y) = \overline{I}_o(\nu_x, \nu_y)\,\overline{L}(\nu_x, \nu_y) \tag{28}$$

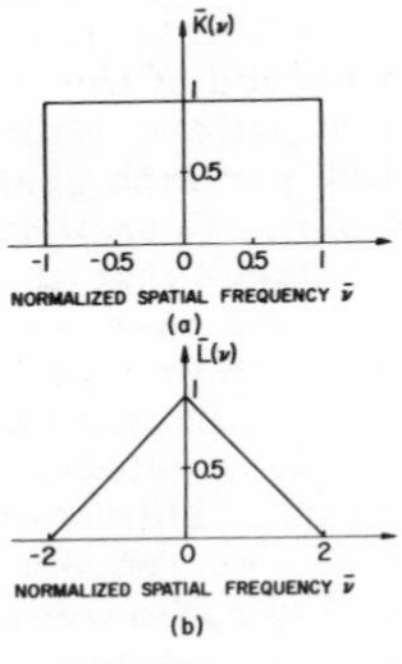

Fig. 10. Frequency responses of a lesn. (a) coherent illumination; (b) incoherent illumination.

The transformation of the object to the image plane is similar to that of equation (27) but applies to the intensities and not to the complex amplitudes. The frequency response function $\overline{L}(\nu_x, \nu_y)$ is given by the autocorrelation function of the pupil function $K(\nu_x, \nu_y)$ [see page 485 Ref. 1]. The normalized frequency responses for coherent and non-coherent illumination are shown in Fig. 10. We can see that in the case of non-coherent illumination the attenuation is different for the different frequencies.

Since we have assumed a perfect lens, the pupil function is real, and there is no shift of phase. Consequently, the image of a sinusoidal object is also sinusoidal, with the same frequency, but attenuated in contrast. There is a maximum frequency beyond which no image can be obtained. The above statement applies to both coherent and non-coherent illuminations, the only difference is that in the latter case, the attenuation is stronger than in the former.

We can now analyze the effect of the superposition of the two gratings. To simplify the analysis let us consider the superposition of the gratings of equations (6) and (13), assumed to be located in the same plane. The resulting transmission function is

$$F_R(x) = F_1(x)\,F_2(x) = a^2 + \frac{a^2}{2}\cos\frac{2\pi x}{p} + \frac{a^2}{2}\cos 2\pi\left[\frac{x}{p} + \overline{\psi}(x)\right] + \frac{a^2}{8}\cos 2\pi\left[\frac{2x}{p} + \overline{\psi}(x)\right] + \frac{a^2}{8}\cos 2\pi\,\overline{\psi}(x) \tag{29}$$

The resulting transmission function contains two terms that correspond to the two superimposed gratings, plus two other terms that have the effect of modulating the complex amplitude of these images. If now we assume that a plane wave front of amplitude E impinges on the two superimposed gratings, the resulting outgoing amplitude is given by

$$E_R = E\,F_R(x) \tag{30}$$

The intensity received by the image plane is

$$I = E_R^2 \tag{31}$$

If we put in the image plane a film to record this intensity, the transmittance function of the film is given by

$$T(x) = k\, I(x)^{-\gamma} = k\,[E_o^2 F_R^2 (x)]^{-\gamma} \tag{32}$$

where γ is the slope of the linear portion of the density vs. the logarithm of the exposure curve and k a constant of proportionality. If we assume that $\gamma = \frac{1}{2}$, the transmittance function of the film becomes identical to the transmission function given by equation (29), except for a constant of proportionality. Fig. 11 shows the record of the light intensity trace of a moiré fringe obtained by scanning a moiré pattern with a microdensitometer. The pattern was produced by a 300 line per inch grating and a 250 magnification has been utilized to obtain the plot. Equation (29) contains the basic features that can be observed in Fig. 11, in this case the carrier is the 300 line per inch grid and the amplitude is modulated. The eye perceives the envelope and this envelope constitutes the moiré fringes. This phenomenon is similar to the beat phenomenon observed in acoustic and radio-engineering.

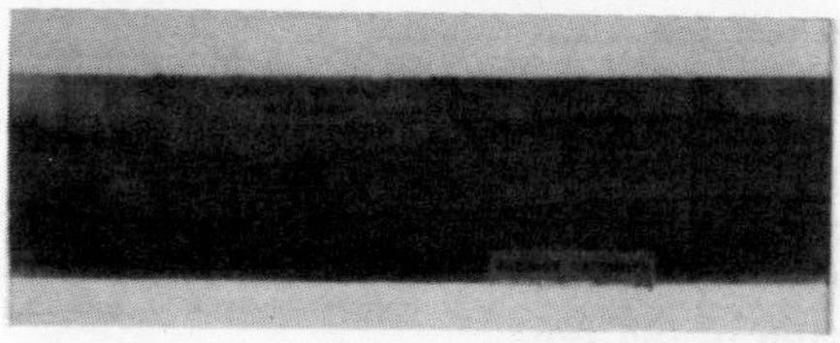

Fig. 11. Microdensitogram along a moiré pattern.

Let us consider now the points of maximum amplitude of the envelope. The period is given by the last term of the equation (29). Each time that

$$\overline{\psi}(x) = n \tag{33a}$$

we have maximum intensity. Recalling equation (24), the maxima correspond to displacements equal to

$$u = np \tag{33b}$$

The minima correspond to displacements equal to

$$u = \left(\frac{2n+1}{2}\right) p \tag{33c}$$

We can see that the moire pattern formation is equivalent to use a cosine function as a basic carrier, the carrier is then modulated by the deformation and finally the integral values of the modulating function are detected by passing the carrier through another grating, a "comb" filter. This operation has the effect of producing a modulating envelope. The envelope can be detected by visual inspection.

In the previous analysis we assumed $\gamma = \frac{1}{2}$, if $\gamma \neq \frac{1}{2}$ the resulting transmission function will contain higher order terms but the obtained conclusion is not modified by the presence of these terms.

We have analyzed the case of coherent illumination. If the illumination is non-coherent, in place of the transmission function, we will consider the transmittance. The final result is similar to the one obtained previously and only the relative intensities of the different terms will be modified. If the grating is not sinusoidal, higher order components will be included in the corresponding terms. If we consider the envelope and disregard the component gratings, the expression of the intensity becomes [2]

$$I(x) = I_o + I_1 \cos 2\pi\, \overline{\psi}(x) + I_2 \cos 4\pi\, \overline{\psi}(x) + I_3 \cos 6\pi\, \overline{\psi}(x) + \ldots \tag{34}$$

A conventional vector picture, Fig. 12, can be used to represent the intensity distribution corresponding to equation (34). I_o represents the background intensity, and the constant amplitude vectors I_1, I_2 ..., represent the amplitudes of the components of the signal. Assuming that all but the fundamental components are eliminated from equation (34), one obtains [2], [3]

$$\theta(x) = 2\pi\, \bar{\psi}(x) = \text{arc cos} \frac{I(x) - I_o}{I_1} \qquad (35)$$

where $\theta(x)$ is the phase of the vector I_1, defined as the angle rotated by the vector from the beginning of the pattern up to the point x. According to equation (24)

$$u(x) = p \frac{\theta(x)}{2\pi} = p\, \bar{\psi}(x) \qquad (36)$$

we can see that by means of the moiré phenomenon we have been able to obtain the modulating function. The modulating function times the pitch of the reference grating gives the projected displacement in the direction of the normal to the reference grating. Each time that

$$\bar{\psi}(x) = n \qquad (37)$$

the intensity will be maximum. When

$$\bar{\psi}(x) = \frac{2n+1}{2} \qquad (38)$$

the intensity will be a minimum.

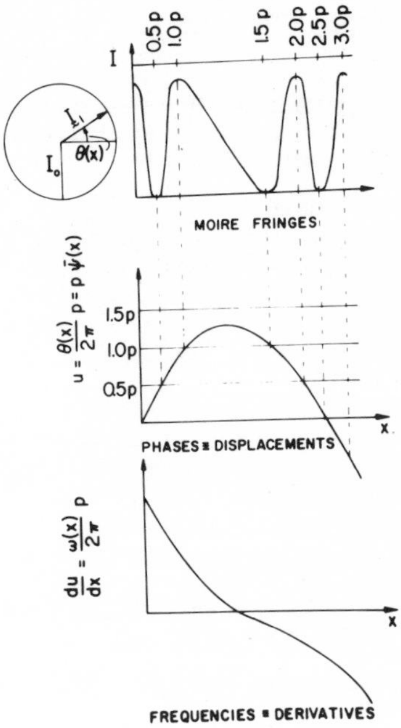

Fig. 12. Vectorial representation of light-intensity trace of a moiré fringe pattern.

We can see that the bright fringes are the loci of points where the projected relative displacements of the points in the direction normal to the reference grating is equal to an integer number times the pitch of the reference grating. The dark fringes have a similar interpretation but in terms of the half pitches. It is interesting to notice that since the model grating is attached to the model, the displacements are given with respect to the deformed shape of the model, and consequently they correspond to the Eulerian description. [4] We have considered only the projected relative displacements in one direction, but to have a complete information we need the projected displacements in another direction. If we work with cartesian coordinates the logical choice is a system of lines perpendicular to the first.

The transmission function of a system of orthogonal lines can be expressed by

$$F(x, y) = C_o + \sum_{m,n=1}^{\infty} C_{mn} \cos 2\pi \frac{x}{p} \cos 2\pi \frac{y}{p} \qquad (39)$$

Following a similar process to that followed to compute the intensity distribution in a moiré pattern produced by a line grating we can show that

$$I(x, y) = I_o + I_1 \cos 2\pi\, \bar{\psi}_x(x, y) \cos 2\pi\, \bar{\psi}_y(x, y) + I_2 \cos 4\pi\, \bar{\psi}_x(x, y) \cos 4\pi\, \bar{\psi}_y(x, y) + \dots \qquad (40)$$

Two families of fringes are observed and their interpretation is similar to the interpretation corresponding to the fringes produced by line gratings. In some cases, the presence of two families of lines may produce confusion in the interpretation and it is preferable to utilize a line reference grating. From the recorded patterns we can obtain $\overline{\psi}_x(x, y)$ and $\overline{\psi}_y(x, y)$. These two functions give a complete description of the relative displacements of the model.

The derivatives of the displacements are given by

$$\frac{\partial u}{\partial x} = p \frac{\partial \overline{\psi}_x(x, y)}{\partial x} , \qquad \frac{\partial u}{\partial y} = p \frac{\partial \overline{\psi}_x(x, y)}{\partial y} \tag{41a}$$

$$\frac{\partial v}{\partial x} = p \frac{\partial \overline{\psi}_y(x, y)}{\partial x} , \qquad \frac{\partial v}{\partial y} = p \frac{\partial \overline{\psi}_y(x, y)}{\partial y} \tag{41b}$$

Where u and v are the projected displacements in the x and y axis respectively.

As shown in equation (26) the direct derivative or derivatives in the direction of the projection axis are related to the frequencies of the frequency modulated signals, Fig. 12. Fig. 13 shows the moiré pattern corresponding to the u displacements of a disc under diametral compression, the corresponding u displacements and the strains obtained as slopes of the displacement curve.

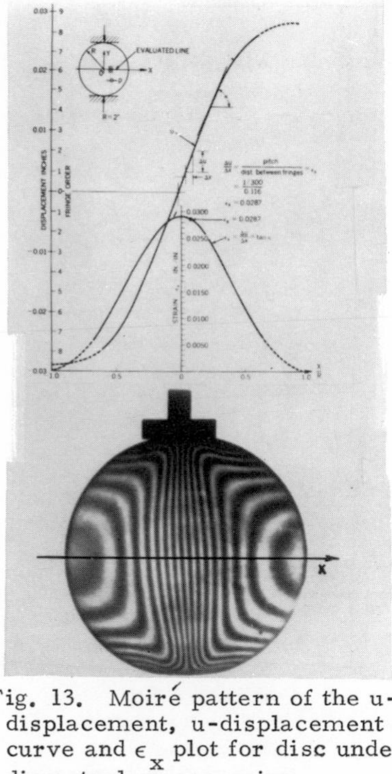

Fig. 13. Moiré pattern of the u-displacement, u-displacement curve and ϵ_x plot for disc under diametral compression.

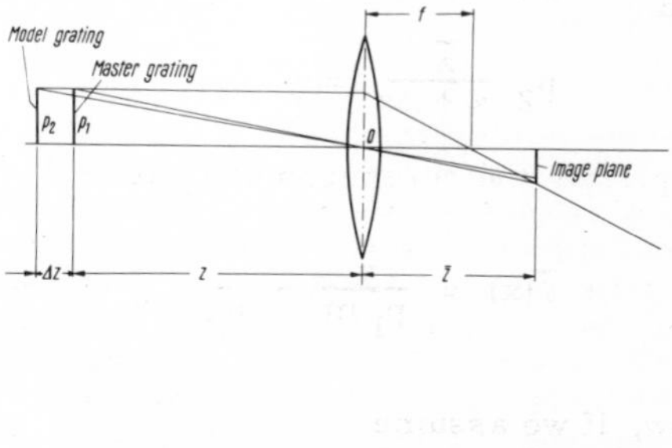

Fig. 14. Optical system forming the image of two superposed gratings.

Effect of the Gap Between Gratings

We assume that the two gratings are no longer in the same plane and that a small gap exists between them, Fig. 14. We assume that we focus the image of the grating closest to the camera, grating 1, and therefore the other grating, grating 2, is not focussed. For this last grating equation (27) applies but a new factor appears [5] which takes into consideration the amount of defocussing. Consequently the complex amplitude at the image plane for the grating that is out of focus is given by

$$\overline{U}_1(\nu_x,\nu_y) = \overline{U}_o(\nu_x,\nu_y)\ \overline{K}(\nu_x,\nu_y)\ \overline{A}(\Delta z,\nu_x,\nu_y) \quad (42)$$

the new added factor $\overline{A}(\Delta z, \nu_x, \nu_y)$ has the effect of decreasing the response of the lens for increasing frequencies. As Δz increases a change of phase is also associated with the defocussing, but if we assume small values of Δz, only the amplitude of the wavefront is affected and not the phase.

Consequently under this assumption the frequency composition of the image is preserved, but in view of the gap existing between the two gratings, a difference in pitch magnification arises. We can go through a similar analysis to the one applied in the preceding section and we get as a final result for the intensity distribution

$$I(x) = I'_o + I'_1 \cos 2\pi \frac{x}{p_2 m'} + I''_1 \cos 2\pi \frac{x}{p_1 m} + \frac{I_2}{2}\cos 2\pi x\left[\frac{1}{p_1 m} + \frac{1}{p_2 m'}\right] + \frac{I_2}{2}\cos 2\pi x\left[\frac{1}{p_1 m} - \frac{1}{p_2 m'}\right] + \ldots \quad (43)$$

Where $p_1 m$ indicates the pitch of grating 1 in the image plane, m being the corresponding magnification and $p_2 m'$ is the pitch of the image of grating 2, m' being the corresponding magnification.

Equation (43) shows that even when $p_1 = p_2$ a pattern will be produced provided $m \neq m'$.

With the notation introduced in Fig. 14, the magnification corresponding to the master grating is given by

$$m = \frac{\overline{z}}{z} \quad (44)$$

then

$$p_1 \frac{\overline{z}}{z} = p_1 m \quad (45)$$

and

$$p_2 \frac{\overline{z}}{z + \Delta z} = p_2 m' \quad (46)$$

Replacing the corresponding values in the expression of $\overline{\psi}$,

$$\overline{\psi}(x) = \frac{x}{p_1 m} - \frac{x}{p_2 m'} = x\left[\frac{1}{p_1 \frac{\overline{z}}{z}} - \frac{1}{p_2 \frac{\overline{z}}{z + \Delta z}}\right] \quad (47)$$

Now, if we assume

$$p_1 = p_2 = p \quad (48)$$

we obtain

$$\overline{\psi}(x) = -x \frac{\Delta z}{p\,\overline{z}} \quad (49)$$

from (45), (48) and (24)

$$u = pm\overline{\psi} \quad (50)$$

and then according to equation (44)

$$u = x\frac{\Delta z}{z} \quad (51)$$

The presence of a gap is equivalent to a fictitious displacement. Consequently a moiré pattern contains not only information on the in-plane displacements but also concerning the displacements in the direction perpendicular to the plane of the grating. Further analysis of this point will be done later. From equation (51) we can see that in order to minimize the effect of the gap we must make the quotient $\Delta z/z$ very small. Since Δz will be always present due to the deformations of the surface in the direction perpendicular to its plane, z must be as large as possible.

APPLICATION OF INFORMATION PROCESSING TECHNIQUES TO MOIRÉ PATTERNS

We have analyzed the basic principles underlying the moiré technique. Now we will consider a number of interesting operations that can be performed by optical means in moiré patterns. These operations can be properly considered as belonging to the general domain of information processing. Such applications rest on the ability of optical systems to perform general linear transformations of input data.

Spatial Filtering: Multiple Orders

The process of filtering described in the section about gratings can be applied to two superimposed gratings and the moiré patterns corresponding to two orthogonal directions can be separated in this way. By allowing to pass only the orders corresponding to one family of lines, the contrast of this family is enhanced and the contrast of the orthogonal family is reduced, Fig. 15.

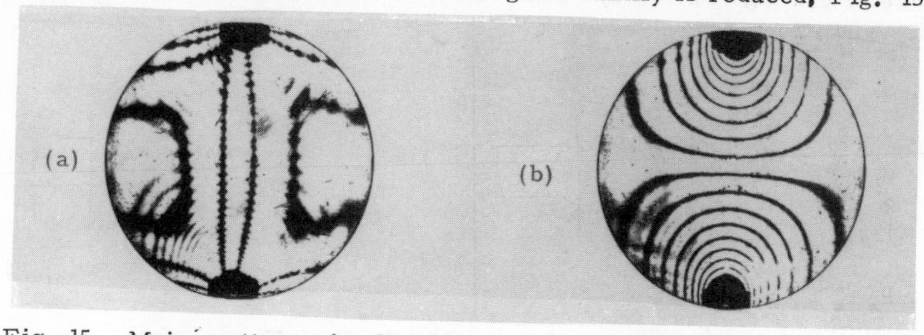

Fig. 15. Moiré pattern of a disc under diametral compression.
(a) u-moiré pattern; (b) v-moiré pattern.

The process of optical filtering can be applied also in the case of non-coherent diffuse illumination. In this case [6], the pupil function of the imaging lens must be modified to obtain the desired result. Inserting a rectangular slit in the plane of the diaphragm of a compound lens, produces the separation of orthogonal families of gratings.

Spatial Filtering: Single Order

Let us suppose now that only one single order in the vertical or horizontal diffraction patterns is allowed to pass [7]. The image of the model together with the moiré pattern will be formed by this single order. We can analyze the formation of the moiré pattern in the following manner. For the sake of simplicity let us consider that the grids are blazed so that all the energy is concentrated in the zero and the first orders. Considering again equation (12), the wave fronts emerging from the first grating can be expressed by

$$\underset{\sim}{E}(x, z) = E_o\, e^{i[\bar{\phi}_o + \frac{2\pi z}{\lambda}]} + E_1\, e^{i[\bar{\phi}_1 + 2\pi \frac{z \cos\theta_1 + x \sin\theta_1}{\lambda}]} + E_1\, e^{i[\bar{\phi}_1 + 2\pi \frac{z \cos\theta_1 - x \sin\theta_1}{\lambda}]} \qquad (52)$$

In equation (52) we have added the constant phases $\bar{\phi}_o$, $\bar{\phi}_1$, which depend on the characteristics of the grooves of the gratings and are added to the relative phases introduced in equation (12) to give the absolute phases of the wave fronts with respect to the incident wave front.

Each of the wave fronts originating from the first grating will generate a similar sequence in the second grating, Fig. 16.

Wave fronts like the sequence, 0, 1, and 1, 0 that emerge along the same path will interefere, producing the moire pattern. Calling ϕ_{01} the resulting phase corresponding to the sequence 0,1 and ϕ_{10} the phase corresponding to the sequence 1, 0, the two interfering wave fronts can be represented by

$$\underset{\sim}{E}_{01} = E_{01}\, e^{i\phi_{01}} \quad (53a)$$

$$\underset{\sim}{E}_{10} = E_{10}\, e^{i\phi_{10}} \quad (53b)$$

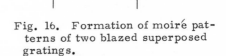

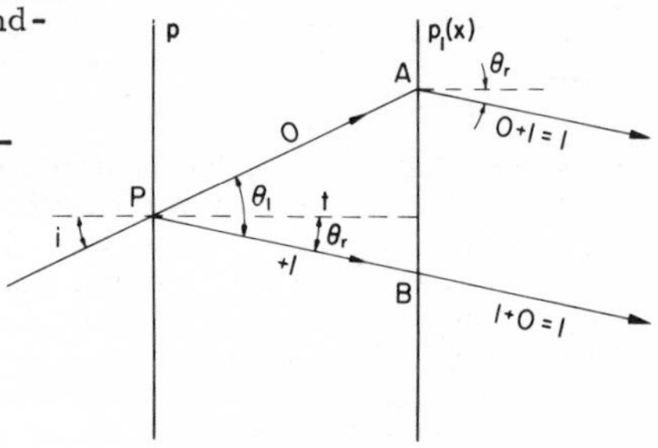

Fig. 16. Formation of moiré patterns of two blazed superposed gratings.

The resultant disturbance at the common point of emergence is given by

$$\underset{\sim}{E}_s = \underset{\sim}{E}_{01} + \underset{\sim}{E}_{10} \quad (54)$$

The observed intensity is equal to

$$I = \underset{\sim}{E}_s^{*} \cdot \underset{\sim}{E}_s \quad (55)$$

After some simple transformation (55) gives

$$I = I_o + I_1 \cos[\phi_{01} - \phi_{10}] \quad (56)$$

But, Fig. 16 gives

$$\phi_{01} = \bar{\phi}_0 + \frac{2\pi}{\lambda}\frac{t}{\cos i} + \bar{\phi}_1 + 2\pi\frac{x}{p_1(x)} \quad (57a)$$

$$\phi_{10} = \bar{\phi}_1 + \frac{2\pi x}{p} + \frac{2\pi}{\lambda}\frac{t}{\cos\theta_r} + \bar{\phi}_0 \quad (57b)$$

where we have expressed the phases in the z direction in terms of the gap between the gratings and we have made use of equation (11).

Replacing (57a) and (57b) in (56) we obtain

$$I = I_o + I_1 \cos 2\pi\left[x\left(\frac{1}{p} - \frac{1}{p_1(x)}\right) + \frac{t}{\lambda}(\cos i - \cos\theta_r)\right] \quad (58)$$

where since i and θ_r are small we have made $\cos i \cos\theta_r \cong 1$.

Not considering the term corresponding to the gap, equation (58) gives the same result as equation (29), if one considers the intensity distribution corresponding to the envelope of the two gratings (moiré effect) present in the image. We must observe that in the present case the image of the gratings has been eliminated by a filtering process. In the utilized optical system only one diffraction order is allowed to pass to the image forming system and at least two orders are needed to produce an image of the gratings.

The effect of the gap can be eliminated if the angles of incidence and emergence are equal in magnitude, [7], [8]. This is the condition illustrated in Fig. 17 and is the condition of minimum deviation for the +1 order of the superposed gratings. It is easy to see that in the condition of minimum deviation

$$\sin i = \sin \theta_r = \sin \frac{\theta_1}{2} = \frac{\lambda}{2p} \tag{59}$$

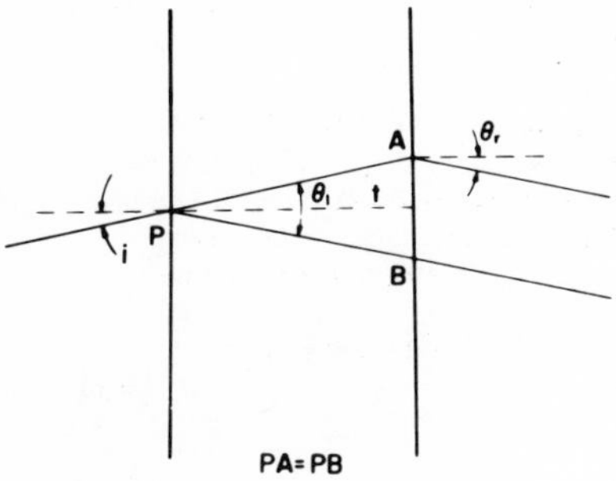

Fig. 17. Minimum deviation angle; elimination of the gap effect.

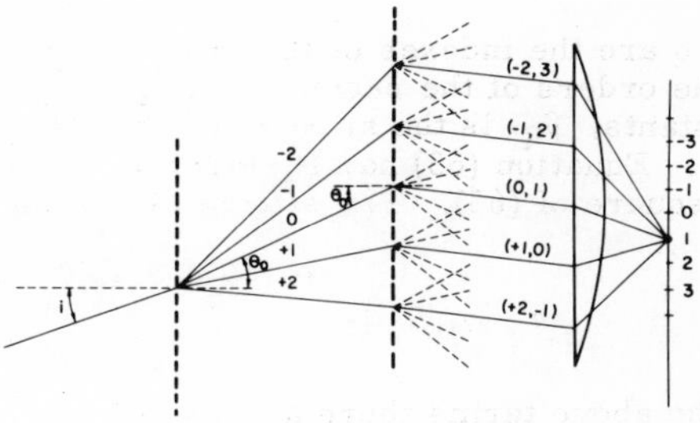

Fig. 18. Multiple orders sequence for the first resulting order.

<u>More general case of pattern formation.</u> In the previous section we considered only two diffraction orders. However, the first grating produces a large number of diffraction orders, let us say n. Of these n orders, the second grating if it is identical to the first will produce another n orders. However, it is very easy to see that the n^2 orders are reduced to n orders. Fig. 18 shows a sequence of orders corresponding to the first order emerging from the second grating. The orders produced by the first grating combine with the orders of the second grating in such a manner that if we call q the order of the first grating and ℓ the corresponding order of the second grating,

$$q + \ell = 1 \tag{60}$$

and in general if the observation is made in the rth order

$$q + \ell = r \tag{61}$$

The two gratings are assumed to be identical and similarly oriented. This last condition is required in the case of gratings with unsymmetrical groove forms with respect to the ends of the gratings [7]. By fulfilling this condition we insure that the diffraction orders in the two gratings have the same distribution with respect to the zero order.

If we assume that the gratings have n significant diffraction orders, and that the observation is made in the rth order, the total number of components forming the rth order is

$$N_r = 2n + 1 - r \tag{62}$$

since the indexes q and ℓ will run respectively from $q = n$, $\ell = r-n$ to $q = r-n$ and $\ell = n$. If r is odd, N_r is even and there are $\frac{2n+1-r}{2}$ symmetrical components. In fact, due to the symmetry of the two gratings the sequence $q + \ell = r$ and $\ell + q = r$ where the first index indicates the first grating and the second index indicates the second grating, are identical.

If r is even, N_r is odd and there is an unpaired component. This component corresponds to the $\frac{r}{2}$ th order and the sequence has $\frac{2n-r}{2}$ symmetrical components. This can be easily checked since if $q = \frac{r}{2}$ then $\ell = \frac{r}{2}$ and there is only one pair of terms in this sequence.

The total amplitude corresponding to the rth order is given by

$$\underset{\sim}{E}_{rt} = \sum_{q=n}^{q=r-n} \sum_{\ell=r-n}^{\ell=n} E_q E_\ell \, e^{i(\Phi_q + \Phi_\ell)} \tag{63}$$

where

$$\Phi_q + \Phi_\ell = \overline{\Phi}_q + \overline{\Phi}_\ell + \frac{2\pi t}{\lambda \cos \beta_q} + 2\pi x \left[\frac{q}{p} + \frac{\ell}{p_1} \right] \tag{64}$$

The q are the indexes of the orders of the first grating, the ℓ are the indexes of the orders of the second grating. $\overline{\Phi}_q$ and $\overline{\Phi}_\ell$ are the corresponding phase constants. β_q is the angle made by the qth order with the normal to the gratings. Equation (63) has N_r terms. The intensity of the rth order is given by the square of (63). The square of the summation leads to terms of the form

$$E_q E_\ell E_i E_k \left[e^{+i\left[(\Phi_q + \Phi_\ell) - (\Phi_i + \Phi_k)\right]} + e^{-i\left[(\Phi_q + \Phi_\ell) - (\Phi_i + \Phi_k)\right]} \right] \tag{65}$$

Of the above terms there are 2n + 1 - r terms for which

$$(\Phi_q + \Phi_\ell) - (\Phi_i + \Phi_k) = 0 \tag{66}$$

These terms contain the squares of the resulting amplitudes. The remaining terms are formed by the combinations of the (2n + 1 - r) terms that form the rth order, taken two at a time. There are

$$N = \frac{(2n + 1 - r)!}{2!\ (2n - r - 1)!} \tag{67}$$

of these kind of terms. The phases of these terms are given by

$$\Phi_R = (\overline{\Phi}_q + \overline{\Phi}_\ell) - (\overline{\Phi}_i + \overline{\Phi}_k) + \frac{2\pi t}{\lambda}\left[\cos \beta_q - \cos \beta_i\right] + 2\pi x \left[\left(\frac{q}{p} + \frac{\ell}{p_1} \right) - \left(\frac{i}{p} + \frac{k}{p_1} \right) \right] \tag{68}$$

where β_q and β_i are assumed to be small. Since

$$q - i = k - \ell \tag{69}$$

the last term of Φ_R can be written

$$2\pi x (q - i) \left[\frac{1}{p} - \frac{1}{p_1} \right] \tag{70}$$

The maximum value of q - i can be easily computed if we make q = n and i = r - n

$$q - i = 2n - r \tag{71}$$

There is only one term containing the highest value of q - i, there are two terms corresponding to the value of

$$q - i = 2n - r - 1 \tag{72}$$

and there is (2n - r) terms for which the order is

$$q - i = 1 \tag{73}$$

With the notation,

$$E_n E_{r-n} = E_n^{r-n} \tag{74}$$

$$\bar{\Phi}_n + \bar{\Phi}_{r-n} = \Phi_n^{r-n} \tag{75}$$

if the order-group selected for observation is being transmitted at the minimum deviation angle, the expression of the resulting intensity can be written

$$\begin{aligned}
I(x) = {} & E_n^{r-n} E_{r-n}^{n} \cos 2\pi\, x\,(2n - r)\left[\frac{1}{p} - \frac{1}{p_1}\right] + \\
& \Bigg\{ E_n^{r-n} E_{r-n+1}^{n-1} \cos\left[(\Phi_n^{r-n} - \Phi_{r-n+1}^{n-1}) + \frac{2\pi t}{\lambda}(\cos\beta_n - \cos\beta_{r-n+1})\right] + \\
& E_{n-1}^{r-n+1} E_{r-n}^{n} \cos\left[(\Phi_{n-1}^{r-n+1} - \Phi_{r-n}^{n}) + \frac{2\pi t}{\lambda}(\cos\beta_{n-1} - \cos\beta_{r-n})\right] \Bigg\} \\
& \cos 2\pi\, x\,(2n - r - 1)\left[\frac{1}{p} - \frac{1}{p_1}\right] + \\
& \Bigg\{ E_n^{r-n} E_{n-1}^{r-n+1} \cos\left[(\Phi_n^{r-n} - \Phi_{n-1}^{r-n+1}) + \frac{2\pi t}{\lambda}(\cos\beta_n - \cos\beta_{n-1})\right] + \\
& E_{n-1}^{r-n+1} E_{r-n+1}^{n-1} + E_{r-n+1}^{n-1} E_{r-n}^{n} \left[\cos(\Phi_{r-n+1}^{n-1} - \Phi_{r-n}^{n}) + \frac{2\pi t}{\lambda}(\cos\beta_{r-n+1} - \right. \\
& \left. \cos\beta_{r-n})\right] \Bigg\} \cos 2\pi\, x\,(2n - r - 2)\left[\frac{1}{p} - \frac{1}{p_1}\right] + \ldots
\end{aligned} \tag{76}$$

The above equation can be simplified if we call I_s the coefficient of the term $\cos 2\pi\, x\, s\left(\frac{1}{p} - \frac{1}{p_1}\right)$

$$\begin{aligned}
I(x) = {} & I_o + I_1 \cos 2\pi x\left[\frac{1}{p} - \frac{1}{p_1}\right] + I_2 \cos 2\pi\; 2x\left[\frac{1}{p} - \frac{1}{p_1}\right] \\
& + \ldots + I_{2n-r} \cos 2\pi\, x\,(2n - r)\left[\frac{1}{p} - \frac{1}{p_1}\right]
\end{aligned} \tag{77}$$

The above equation gives the intensity distribution of the rth order, produced by two identical and similarly oriented gratings, with n active diffraction orders, and viewed through the minimum deviation angle corresponding to the rth order. The resulting fringes depend on the particular values and signs of the coefficients, which in turn depend on the characteristics of the gratings. They also depend on the gap, even under minimum deviation conditions. In fact, only the terms that result from the combination of symmetrical orders do not contain the effect of the gap. The non-symmetrical combinations include the gap effect and the higher the order of the term, the more important the effect of the gap.

Although it is necessary to have a complete information concerning amplitudes and phase constants of a grating to determine the intensity distribution of the resulting interference system, equation (77) provides a very useful tool to discuss possible fringe systems in many cases of interest, (see Ref. [6]).

Optical Differentiation

In the previous sections we have utilized a reference grating identical to the model grating, to detect the changes experienced by the model grating under the applied loads. A different method will be described now, [9], [10], [11], [12].

Let us suppose that we make two contact copies of a deformed grating and that we introduce a shift between the two copies in the direction perpendicular to the grating lines. To simplify the analysis we will consider sinusoidal gratings. We assume that we make the copies with coherent monochromatic light. We can represent the wavefronts emerging from the model

$$\underset{\sim}{E}_1(x) = E_o + E_1 e^{-2\pi i \frac{(x+\Delta x)}{p_1(x)}} + E_1 e^{2\pi i \frac{(x+\Delta x)}{p_1(x)}} \tag{78}$$

$$\underset{\sim}{E}_2(x) = E_o + E_1 e^{-2\pi i \frac{(x-\Delta x)}{p_1(x)}} + E_1 e^{2\pi i \frac{(x-\Delta x)}{p_1(x)}} \tag{79}$$

where $\Delta x = \frac{\overline{\Delta x}}{2}$, $\overline{\Delta x}$ being the shift introduced between the two copies. We have assumed that the contribution of the z coordinate is negligible, (contact copying).

The resulting intensity received by the photographic plate in the first exposure is

$$I(x+\Delta x) = E_o^2 + 2E_1^2 + 4E_oE_1 \cos 2\pi \left[\frac{x+\Delta x}{p_1(x)}\right] + 2E_1^2 \cos 4\pi \left[\frac{x+\Delta x}{p_1(x)}\right] \tag{80}$$

Similarly in the second exposure

$$I(x-\Delta x) = E_o^2 + 2E_1^2 + 4E_oE_1 \cos 2\pi \left[\frac{x-\Delta x}{p_1(x)}\right] + 2E_1^2 \cos 4\pi \left[\frac{x-\Delta x}{p_1(x)}\right] \tag{81}$$

The resulting intensity received by the plate during the two exposures is

$$I_R(x) = I(x+\Delta x) + I(x-\Delta x) \tag{82}$$

The energy received by the photographic plate produces, after the developing process, the transmission function

$$F(x) = I(x)^{-\frac{\gamma}{2}} \tag{83}$$

where γ is the slope of the density vs. the logarithm of the exposure curve. In order to simplify the derivation of the equations we can assume $\gamma = -2$ and F(x) in equation (83) becomes identical to I(x) in equation (82).

To observe the corresponding pattern we will utilize a set-up similar to the one employed to observe moiré fringes with coherent monochromatic collimated light. Let us consider that we make the observation in the +1 order, the following wavefronts are combined

$$\underset{\sim}{E}_{1R} = E_1 e^{2\pi i \frac{(x+\Delta x)}{p_1(x)}} + E_1 e^{2\pi i \frac{(x-\Delta x)}{p_1(x)}} \tag{84}$$

Computing the corresponding intensity we obtain

$$I_{1R}(x) = 2E_1^2 + 2E_1^2 \cos 2\pi \left[\frac{x + \Delta x}{p_1(x)} - \frac{x - \Delta x}{p_1(x)} \right] \tag{85}$$

but

$$\frac{x + \Delta x}{p_1(x)} = \bar{\psi}\,(x + \Delta x) + \frac{x + \Delta x}{p} \tag{86a}$$

and

$$\frac{x - \Delta x}{p_1(x)} = \bar{\psi}\,(x - \Delta x) + \frac{x - \Delta x}{p} \tag{86b}$$

then

$$\frac{x + \Delta x}{p_1(x)} - \frac{x - \Delta x}{p_1(x)} = \bar{\psi}\,(x + \Delta x) - \bar{\psi}\,(x - \Delta x) \tag{87}$$

but according to the mean value theorem of the differential calculus we can write

$$\frac{\bar{\psi}\,(x + \Delta x) - \bar{\psi}\,(x - \Delta x)}{2\,\Delta x} = \frac{\partial\,\bar{\psi}\,(x + \theta\,2\Delta x)}{\partial x}, \quad 0 < \theta < 1 \tag{88}$$

and recalling equation (26), the argument of the cosine term of equation (85) can be written

$$I_{1R}(x) = 2E_1^2 + 2E_1^2 \cos 2\pi \left[\frac{2\Delta x}{p}\, \epsilon_x\, (x + \theta\, 2\Delta x) \right] \tag{89}$$

The pattern observed in the first order corresponds to the direct derivatives measured with the scale $\frac{2\Delta x}{p}$, however, this is only an approximation since the values of the obtained derivatives correspond to points when location is only known within the interval $2\Delta x$. The smaller is the shear $2\Delta x$, the closer are the obtained values to the true derivatives. If the shift is given in the direction of the gratings we can show that

$$I(y) = 2E_1^2 + 2E_1^2 \cos 2\pi \left[\frac{2\,\Delta y}{p}\, \frac{\partial u}{\partial y}\, (y + \theta\, 2\Delta y) \right] \tag{90}$$

In the previous derivations the process of differentiation has been analyzed from the point of view of shearing interferometry. We have taken advantage of the ability of shearing interferograms of displaying the phase gradients of the interfering wavefronts. A similar derivation can be made for non-coherent diffuse light.

We have seen that the contour lines of the partial derivatives of the displacements can be obtained directly as moiré fringes of the shifted deformed gratings. Figure 19 shows the derivatives corresponding to a ring under diametral compression. For a more comprehensive analysis see Ref. [12].

Methods of Increasing the Accuracy and Sensitivity of the Moiré Fringe Technique

We can utilize the moiré method to measure displacements or to compute partial derivatives. In both cases, the sensitivity of the method depends on the pitch of the grating utilized as a carrier.

If we look at equations (35) and (36) we can see that the displacement information is given by the phase of the vector I_1. Both the sensitivity and the accuracy with which the phase can be determined depend on the ratio of the "noise" level to the signal level. Here we must indicate two alternative paths that we can follow in the process of interpretation of moiré patterns. We can consider only

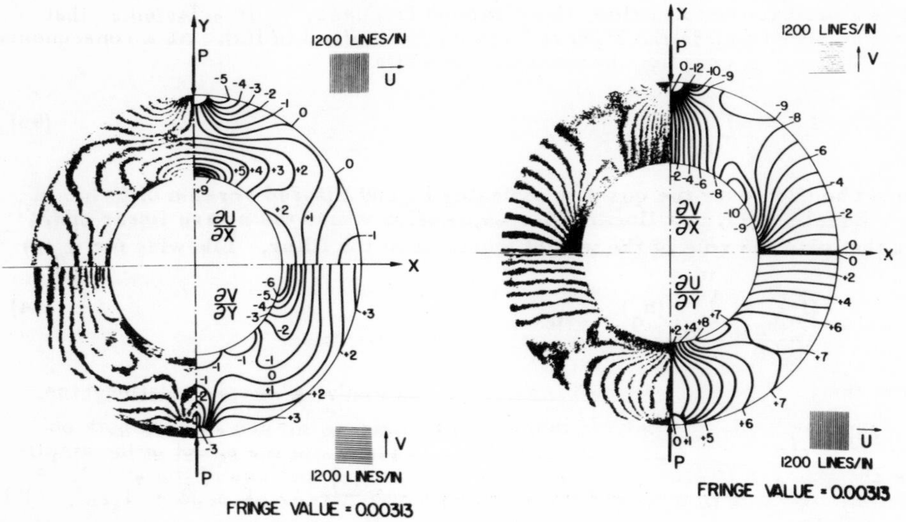

Fig. 19. Pattern of the derivatives of displacements.

maxima and minima of intensity, and thus obtain points where the phase has integer values n or half integers. Alternately we can determine the phase of the vector as a continuous variable. In the second case, of course, both the accuracy and the sensitivity is increased since we increase the amount of information that we gather from a pattern.

Numerical Techniques. Equation (35) could be applied to the retrieval of information from moire data if the only effect modulating the intensity distribution were the frequency modulation of the carrier by the applied loads. [13]. In practice, if we analyze a light intensity record, we can see that besides the frequency modulation there are many sources of amplitude modulation that are not related to the displacement field but depend on the properties of the different elements that are present in the optical system, light source, model lenses, etc. All these sources introduce an unwanted portion of the signal, or "noise".

Since the information that is to be determined is contained in the instantaneous phase of the vector I_1, we must apply a process to separate phase and amplitude information, [14], [15]. This can be achieved by replacing the actual signal by a complex signal of the form [3]

$$\bar{I}(x) = I(x) + I_q(x) \tag{91}$$

where I_q is a signal in quadrature with I(x), then the instantaneous phase is defined as

$$\theta(x) = \text{arc tg} \frac{I_q(x)}{I(x)} \tag{92}$$

Knowing the in-phase component (actual signal) it is possible to find the quadrature signal since they are related through the Hilbert transform. Consequently, any changes in the amplitude of I(x) will occur also in $I_q(x)$ and the phase determination is not affected by the amplitude changes. However, the noise not only affects the amplitude of the vector but also the phase. Our aim is to separate the useful information from the unwanted noise. This goal can be achieved by the process of numerical filtering. For example, to eliminate all the components of the "noise" that have frequencies that do not overlap with the frequency of the signal, numerical bandpass filters can be utilized.

In the numerical process a sampled version of I(x) is utilized and since I(x) is a band limited function, the sampling frequency ν_s is selected so that $\nu_s > 2\nu_c$, where ν_c is the highest frequency contained in I(x). As a consequence of the Shannon's sampling theorem we can write

$$\tilde{I}_k = \sum_{p=-m}^{m} h_p I_{k+p} \tag{93}$$

where the tilde over the quantity indicates a good filtered version of I(x).

Equation (93) is a linear filter expression where the h_p are linear operators that play the role of the weight functions of the filter. Likewise for $I_q(x)$

$$(\tilde{I}_q)_k = \sum_{p=-m}^{m} (h_q)_p I_{k+p} \tag{94}$$

where the $(h_q)_p$ can be obtained from the h_p by applying simple relationships.

Consequently by applying numerical techniques we can achieve both objectives to obtain the signals in quadrature to eliminate the effect of the amplitude changes and to eliminate the effect of unwanted portions of the signal. A different approach to numerically retrieve moiré data is presented in [16].

<u>Optical interpolation.</u> The optical system utilized in the fringe interpolation process is shown in Figure 20. Let us consider the basic elements of the system. [17].

The lens L_1 produces a beam of collimated, monochromatic light which illuminates the master grating G_1. Lens L_2 and L_3 form a system of unit magnification which produces an image of the master grating. The image, together with the model grating, produces moiré fringes which, by means of the field lens L_4 are imaged into the camera C. In order to achieve the interpolation, the following elements are added to the optical system. The light source S is linearly polarized by a polarizer P. A stop is located at the plane F_2 so that only two diffraction orders are allowed to pass. Two quarter wave plates are placed in the focal plane F_2 so that each one of the orders passes through a quarter wave plate. The axis of the quarter-wave plates are oriented in such a way that one of the orders is right circularly polarized while the other is left circularly polarized.

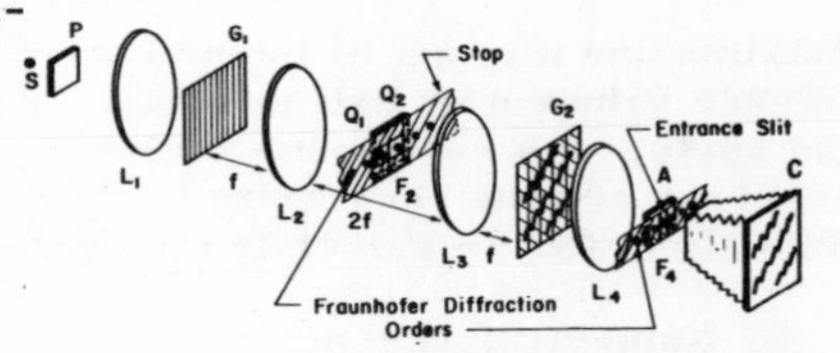

Fig. 20. Optical system for fringe interpolation.

The linear analyzer A, located in front of the camera, resolves the components of the light vector along its polarizing axis. The position of the analyzer is defined by its angle of rotation α with respect to a reference plane. To derive the corresponding equations we assume that the 0 and the +1 orders are allowed to pass and the observation is made in the +1 order. To represent the circularly polarized wave fronts we must remember that we must utilize two orthogonal vectors

$$\underset{\sim}{E}_o = E_o e^{i\Phi_o} \tag{95a}$$

$$(E_o)_q = E_o e^{i(\Phi_o + \frac{\pi}{2})} \tag{95b}$$

$$\underset{\sim}{E}_1 = E_1 \, e^{i(\Phi_1 + 2\pi \frac{x}{p})} \tag{96a}$$

$$(\underset{\sim}{E}_1)_q = E_1 \, e^{i(\Phi_1 + 2\pi \frac{x}{p} - \frac{\pi}{2})} \tag{96b}$$

The sequence 0, 1 can be represented by

$$\underset{\sim}{E}_{01} = E_{01} \, e^{i[\Phi_o + \Phi_1 + 2\pi \frac{x}{p_1(x)}]} \tag{97a}$$

$$[E_{01}]_q = E_{01} \, e^{i[\Phi_o + \Phi_1 + 2\pi \frac{x}{p_1(x)} + \frac{\pi}{2}]} \tag{97b}$$

and the sequence 1, 0 by

$$\underset{\sim}{E}_{10} = E_{10} \, e^{i[\Phi_o + \Phi_1 + 2\pi \frac{x}{p}]} \tag{98a}$$

$$[\underset{\sim}{E}_{10}]_q = E_{10} \, e^{i[\Phi_o + \Phi_1 + 2\pi \frac{x}{p} - \frac{\pi}{2}]} \tag{98b}$$

The two circularly polarized wavefronts $\underset{\sim}{E}_{01}$ and $\underset{\sim}{E}_{10}$ are projected along the direction of the analyzer, defined by the angle α that the analyzer makes with the x axis. To project the circularly polarized wavefronts we multiply (97a) by $e^{i\alpha}$ and (97b) by $e^{i(\alpha - \frac{\pi}{2})}$, (98a) by $e^{-i\alpha}$ and (98b) by $e^{-i(\alpha - \frac{\pi}{2})}$. The resulting vectors are

$$\underset{\sim}{E}_{01} = E_{01} \, e^{i[\Phi_o + \Phi_1 + \frac{2\pi x}{p_1(x)} + \alpha]} \tag{99a}$$

$$\underset{\sim}{E}_{10} = E_{10} \, e^{i[\Phi_o + \Phi_1 + \frac{2\pi x}{p} - \alpha]} \tag{99b}$$

Computing the light intensity distribution and following the same steps applied previously we obtain

$$I(x) = I_o + I_1 \cos [2\pi \overline{\psi}(x) + 2\alpha] \tag{100}$$

Equation (100) is analogous to equation (58) without the gap term but with an additional terms 2α, in the argument of the cosine function. We notice that by rotating the analyzer through an angle α, the cosine term in the intensity function changes by 2α. If the analyzer is rotated through 90 deg., the light fringes will become dark and vice-versa.

In figure 21, the principle employed in the fringe interpolation is illustrated. The displacement curve of a moiré pattern is represented. The horizontal axis represent distances along the line of analysis measured from a fixed point. Each division of the vertical axis represents a displacement of one pitch. According to equation (100) a rotation of the analyzer produces a shift of the moiré pattern. The rotation α of the analyzer is equivalent to shifting the vertical axis of the magnitude $\frac{\alpha p}{180}$ and provides a new set of points. For different approaches to interpolation see [18], [19].

Fringe multiplication. Another possibility offered by the described system is fringe multiplication. We can eliminate all the orders produced by the first grating but two symmetrical orders; let us say +n and -n. If we make our observation in the n + n order, the interfering wavefronts are [17]

$$\underset{\sim}{E}_{-n+n} = E_{-n}^{+n}\, e^{i[\Phi_{-n}^{+n} - \frac{nx}{p} + \frac{nx}{p_1(x)}]} \quad (101)$$

$$\underset{\sim}{E}_{+n-n} = E_{+n}^{-n}\, e^{i[\Phi_{+n}^{-n} + \frac{nx}{p} - \frac{nx}{p_1(x)}]} \quad (102)$$

where the notation introduced in equations (76) has been utilized. The resulting intensity is

$$I(x) = I_o + I_n \cos 2\pi\ 2nx\left[\frac{1}{p} - \frac{1}{p_1(x)}\right] \quad (103)$$

Consequently, 2n times as many fringes will be observed as in the fundamental pattern. We can see that the same effect can be achieved without the projecting lens system if we use as a reference grating a grating such that it has for example a pitch of order $\frac{p}{n}$ and is blazed for example for the 0 and +1 orders. If we arrange the corresponding optical system for minimum deviation, the same result corresponding to equation (103) is obtained for such a pair of gratings.[20].

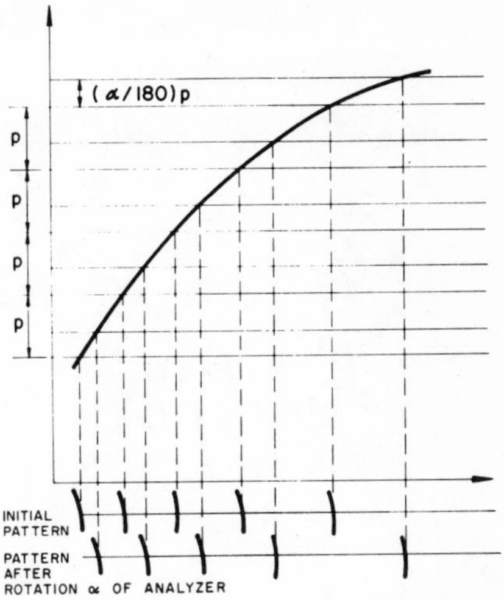

Fig. 21. Graphical interpretation of the fringe interpolation process.

One of the disadvantages of the lens system is that the aberrations of the lenses produce distorted moiré patterns. There are two possible ways of correcting this effect. One possible solution is to introduce an initial pattern in the plane of the model image. This can be done by rotating the master grating with respect to the model grating. [21]. In this way one can generate a moiré pattern with a large number of fringes for the unloaded model. If we load the model and we superimpose the two patterns, we obtain a pattern free from the aberrations. In fact the only changes introduced between the loaded and the unloaded conditions are produced by the applied loads.

An alternative way is to eliminate the master grating and to put in its place the model [22]. The image of the unloaded model is recorded on a photographic plate. The loaded model is recorded again in the same plate. The moiré pattern is observed in coherent collimated light as shown in Fig. 22. Several lens arrangements can be utilized in this technique; some of these arrangements are more advantageous than others concerning the maximum multiplication that can be achieved [22]. Examples of fringe multiplication are shown in Fig. 23. This method can be utilized to separate the patterns corresponding to orthogonal gratings [28], or to generate patterns corresponding to a previously selected direction as it was shown in Fig. 7. In this way we can obtain three patterns equivalent to a rosette [23].

<u>Mismatch.</u> An alternative possibility to improve the accuracy and the sensitivity of the moiré method, is to work with the change of the fringe spacing, rather than with the fringe spacing itself, [24], [25], [26]. Let us suppose that the model and master gratings have slightly different pitches; an

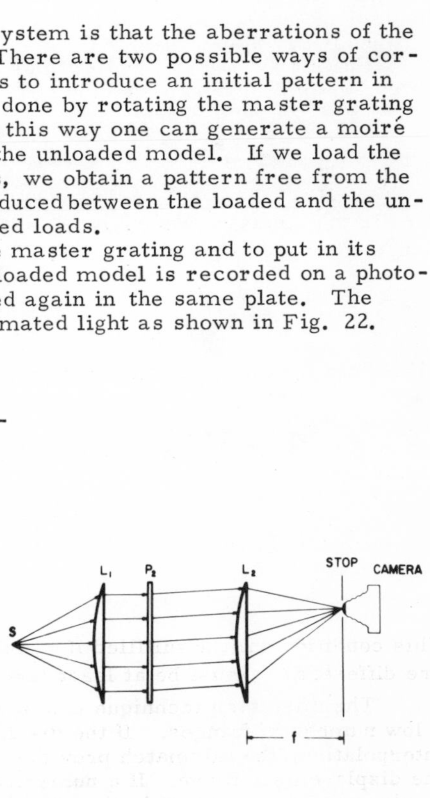

Fig. 22. Optical system utilized in the fringe-multiplication process and in the 3-D moiré

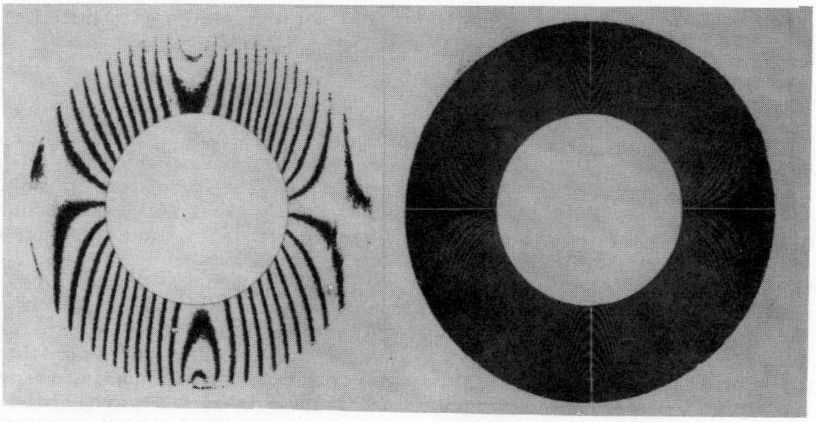

(a) 600 l. p. i.

(b) 6000 l. p. i.

Fig. 23. Ring under diametral compression
(a) Multiplication by 2
(b) Multiplication by 20

initial moiré pattern of parallel fringes will be present. We assume that the strains are small and that the moiré pattern has been referred to the initial or undeformed state.

Calling ϵ_m the initial fictitious strain corresponding to the pitch mismatch, the initial fringe spacing is

$$\delta_m = \frac{p}{|\epsilon_m|} \tag{104}$$

If ϵ_d is the strain produced by the applied deformation, the corresponding fringe spacing is

$$\delta_d = \frac{p}{|\epsilon_d|} \tag{105}$$

The fringe spacing resulting from the superposition of ϵ_m and ϵ_d is equal to

$$\delta_f = \frac{p}{|\epsilon_m| \pm |\epsilon_d|} \tag{106}$$

The plus sign is applied when $\epsilon_m \epsilon_d > 0$; the minus sign when $\epsilon_m \epsilon_d < 0$. The pitch mismatch is useful only if

$$\delta_f < \delta_d \tag{107}$$

This condition will be fulfilled if ϵ_m and ϵ_d have the same sign. If the signs are different, ϵ_m must be at least larger than $2\epsilon_d$.

The mismatch technique can be useful in cases where the patterns show a low number of fringes. If the displacement curve is plotted by graphical interpolation, the mismatch provides an increasing number of points to define the displacement curve. If a numerical technique is applied, the mismatch can produce an improvement in the signal to noise ratio.

To increase the number of moiré fringes it is also possible to introduce a rotation of the master grating relative to the specimen grating [26], [27].

This corresponds to a rigid-body motion and is not associated with initial strains.

THREE DIMENSIONAL ANALYSIS

Up to this point we have concerned ourselves with two dimensional problems, and we have postulated conditions of observation under which the effect of the displacement in the third dimension can be ignored for all practical purposes. We will consider now the more general case and we will assume that coherent collimated light is utilized in the observation of the moiré phenomenon [28].

We will assume that we have a grating printed in a plane that may be located inside of a model or in the surface of a model. When the model is loaded the points of the grating experience displacements u, v and w parallel to the x, y and z axis, respectively. We assume that the plane of the grating is the xy plane and that the grating lines are parallel to the x and y axis, respectively. If a plane wave-front impinges on the grating in such a way that the plane of incidence is not a principal plane (plane perpendicular to the grating lines in the x or the y direction) Fig. 24, equation (11) must be replaced by the following system of equations

$$\sin \theta'_n = \sin \theta'_i \qquad (108a)$$

$$\sin \theta''_n = \sin \theta''_i + \frac{n\lambda}{p} \qquad (108b)$$

where θ'_i, θ''_i are the angles defining the incident beam with respect to the planes π_1, π_2, called principal plane and secondary plane, respectively, and θ'_n, θ''_n, are the angles defining the diffracted order n with respect to the same planes. For small deformations and rotations, when $\theta'_i = \theta'_n \cong 0$, then $\theta''_i \cong \theta_i$, where θ_i is the angle between the projection of the incident beam on the plane π_1 and the normal to the plane of the grating. Also $\theta''_n = \theta_n$, where θ_n is the angle between the projection of the diffracted beam of order n on the plane π_1 and the normal to the plane of the grating.

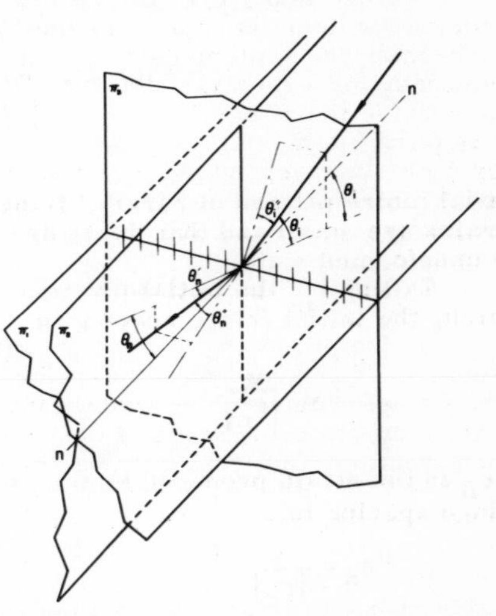

Fig. 24. Angles defining position of incident and diffracted wave fronts for wave fronts of arbitrary orientation.

If we apply the preceding conclusions to the analysis of the local changes of the model grating, we can see Fig. 25, that in the deformed position the plane of the model grating is rotated by an angle θ_i, which is the same angle that the incident wave-front makes with the normal to the deformed grating n'n'. Applying equation (108b) we obtain

$$\sin \theta_{n'} - \sin \theta_i = \frac{n'\lambda}{p} \qquad (109)$$

This equation defines the diffraction order n' with respect to the deformed position of the grating. If we observe Fig. 25, we can see that this order would coincide with the order n, generated by a grating located in the undeformed position and having a pitch

$$p' = p \cos \theta_i \qquad (110)$$

With the foregoing considerations, we can express the wave-fronts emerging from the deformed grating, Fig. 5.

$$E(x_o + u,\; z+w) = E_o\, e^{2\pi i \frac{z+w}{\lambda}} + \sum_{j=1}^{j=N} E_j\, e^{\frac{2\pi i (z+w)\cos\theta_j + (x_o+u)\sin\theta_j}{\lambda}} + \sum_{j=1}^{j=N} E_j\, e^{\frac{2\pi i (z+w)\cos\theta_j - (x_o+u)\sin\theta_j}{\lambda}} \tag{111}$$

where the θ_j are defined by the equation

$$\sin\theta_j = \frac{j\lambda}{p\cos\theta_i} \tag{112}$$

and where the x_o indicate the coordinates of the points in the undeformed condition.

We can see that while the zero order wave-front carries information concerning the w displacements, the remaining orders carry information concerning the w and the u displacement. It is possible to write similar equations for a grating perpendicular to the one under consideration and thus, to get information concerning the v displacement.

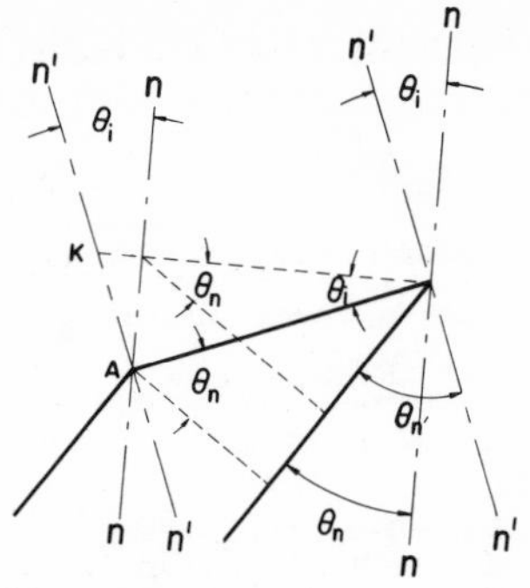

Fig. 25. Effect of rotation of plane of the grating.

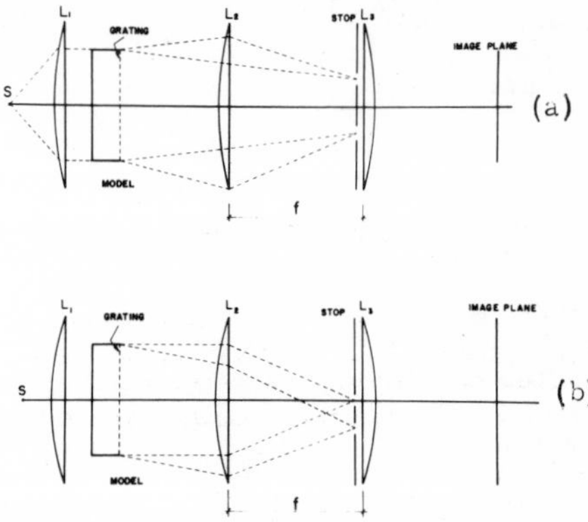

Fig. 26. Optical system utilized in the 3-D moire method

Determination of u and v

In the preceding section we have seen that the wave-fronts emerging from a deformed grating contain information on two projections of the displacement vector. Our goal is to be able to recover this information under the form of separate patterns. To achieve this purpose we can take advantage of the idea of optical filtering, Fig. 26(a). The model grating is illuminated by coherent and monochromatic light, and produces, in the focal plane of the lens L_2, a diffraction pattern. All but two symmetrical orders with respect to the zero order are eliminated and depending on the selected plane, the u or the v patterns will be obtained. These two orders, when collected in the image plane, will produce an image of the model and of the grating printed on it. The process is repeated twice; the first time in the unloaded condition, and a second time in the loaded condition. The two gratings interfere and produce moiré fringes that can be observed by putting the developed photographic plate in the same optical system as in Fig. 26(a). As it will be shown, three diffraction orders can be observed; the zero order and two symmetrical orders. Each of the symmetrical orders contains an image of the model with a moiré pattern corresponding to the u or the v pattern, depending on the plane of observation.

Assuming that the u displacements are observed, and that the two symmetrical orders are the +n and the -n, the wave-fronts that are allowed to pass the filter are

$$\underset{\sim}{E}_n(x, z) = E_n\, e^{2\pi i \frac{z}{\lambda}\cos\theta_n}\, e^{-2\pi i \frac{n x_o}{p}} \tag{113a}$$

$$\underset{\sim}{E}_{-n}(x, z) = E_n\, e^{2\pi i \frac{z}{\lambda}\cos\theta_n}\, e^{2\pi i \frac{n x_o}{p}} \tag{113b}$$

The intensity recorded in the film is

$$I_1(x) = 2E_n^2 [1 + \cos \frac{2\pi \; 2n x_o}{p}] \quad (114)$$

In the second step, the wave-fronts going through the filter are

$$\underset{\sim}{\bar{E}}_n(x, z) = E_n \, e^{2\pi i \frac{1}{\lambda}(z+w)\cos\theta_n} \, e^{-2\pi i \frac{n(x_o + u)}{p(x)}} \quad (115a)$$

$$\underset{\sim}{\bar{E}}_n(x, z) = E_n \, e^{2\pi i \frac{1}{\lambda}(z+w)\cos\theta_n} \, e^{2\pi i \frac{n(x_o + u)}{p(x)}} \quad (115b)$$

Similar to previous derivations, the intensity recorded in the film is

$$I(x) = 2E_n^2 [1 + \cos 2\pi \frac{2nx}{p(x)}] \quad (116)$$

where

$$x = x_o + u \quad (117)$$

The total intensity received by the plate is

$$I(x) = I_1(x) + I_2(x) \quad (118)$$

After developing the transmission function is given by equation (83), and by making the same simplifying assumption previously done, F(x) becomes identical with I(x)

$$F(x) = 2E_n^2 [2 + \cos 2\pi \frac{2nx}{p} + \cos 2\pi \frac{2nx}{p(x)}] \quad (119)$$

In the reconstruction process the photographic plate is placed in collimated light. In the focal plane of lens L_2, Fig. 26(a), a diffraction pattern consisting of three orders is observed.

In the +1 image we receive the following wave-fronts,

$$\underset{\sim}{E}_{1R} = E_n^2 [e^{-2\pi i \frac{2nx}{p}} + e^{-2\pi i \frac{2nx}{p(x)}}] \quad (120)$$

The intensity distribution is

$$I(x) = 2E_n^2 + 2E_n^2 \cos 2\pi x [\frac{2n}{p(x)} - \frac{2n}{p}] \quad (121)$$

We can see that the argument of the cosine function of equation (121) only contains information concerning the u displacements. We can look at the system of lenses of Fig. 26a as producing a Fourier spectrum of the model grating. This spectrum contains information of the spatial frequencies in the plane of the grating. By putting a stop that allows to pass only frequencies related to the x axis direction, we have eliminated all other information. However, as we see from equations (117), information concerning the w displacements is contained in the wave-fronts and allowed to pass. The fact that the w information has disappeared from equation (121) is due to the symmetry of the optical paths of the system of Fig. 26a. The interference fringes produced by the two orders display only the difference of phases between the two wave-fronts, and the phase factor corresponding to w is the same in the two wave-fronts. Consequently, by the described process, the u and v displacements can be obtained in an arbitrarily deformed plane. Of course, we are not limited to the displacement along the x and y axis. By allowing other orders rather than the orders situated along these axis in the frequency plane we can generate other patterns corresponding to axis arbitrarily located with respect to the x-y system, Fig. 7.

Determination of the w Displacements

To obtain the w displacements three steps are applied. In the first step the model is loaded and two nth symmetrical orders are allowed to pass. These two orders produce an image of the deformed grating. In the second, with the model always loaded, Fig. 26(b), the zero and the 2 nth orders are allowed to pass. In the reconstruction process these two gratings interfere, producing a pattern that is function of w alone.

In the first step, the following wave-fronts are made to interfere

$$\underset{\sim}{E}_n(x,z) = E_n\, e^{\frac{2\pi i}{\lambda}(z+w)\cos\theta_n}\, e^{-2\pi i \frac{xn}{p(x)}} \tag{122a}$$

$$\underset{\sim}{E}_{-n}(x,z) = E_n\, e^{\frac{2\pi i}{\lambda}(z+w)\cos\theta_n}\, e^{2\pi i \frac{xn}{p(x)}} \tag{122b}$$

The resulting intensity is

$$I_1(x) = 2E_n^2\left[1 + \cos 2\pi \frac{2nx}{p(x)}\right] \tag{123}$$

In the second step, the interfering wave-fronts are

$$\underset{\sim}{E}_o = E_o\, e^{\frac{2\pi i}{\lambda}(z+w)} \tag{124a}$$

$$\underset{\sim}{E}_{2n} = E_{2n}\, e^{\frac{2\pi i}{\lambda}(z+w)\cos\theta_{2n}}\, e^{-2\pi i \frac{2nx}{p(x)}} \tag{124b}$$

The resulting intensity is

$$I(x) = E_o^2 + E_{2n}^2 + 2E_n E_{2n}$$

$$\times \cos 2\pi\left[\frac{2nx}{p(x)} + (z+w)\frac{1-\cos\theta_{2n}}{\lambda}\right] \tag{125}$$

The total intensity recorded in the plate is given by the sum of equations (123) and (125). In the reconstruction process, the interfering wave-fronts are

$$\underset{\sim}{E}_n = E_n\, e^{-2\pi i \frac{2nx}{p(x)}} \tag{126}$$

and

$$\underset{\sim}{E}_{2n} = E_{2n}\, e^{-2\pi i\left[\frac{2nx}{p(x)} + (z+w)\frac{1-\cos\theta_{2n}}{\lambda}\right]} \tag{127}$$

The resulting intensity is

$$I(x) = E_n^2 + E_{2n}^2 + 2E_n E_{2n} \cos\left[2\pi (z+w)\frac{1-\cos\theta_{2n}}{\lambda}\right] \tag{128}$$

For a given z, a maximum intensity is observed each time

$$w = \frac{k\lambda}{1-\cos\theta_{2n}} \tag{129}$$

By a suitable combination of orders we have been able to separate the w displacements from the u displacements. However, we must remember that in order to produce the filtering process we have introduced lenses. Since in the second step we introduce a non-symmetrical path, the effect of the difference of paths due to the lenses will be displayed in the final pattern. Consequently, to find the w it will be necessary to repeat the process for the model unloaded and loaded. If the initial pattern has many fringes an optical subtraction of the two patterns can be performed.

Fig. 27 shows an application of this technique to the case of a clamped circular plate loaded in the center with a concentrated load. Figs. 27a and 27b show the u and v displacement patterns. In view of the symmetry conditions both patterns must be identical. The slight differences observed in the patterns are due to small imperfections in the load and edge conditions.

A 1000 line per in. grating was printed on the plate, and since orders +2 and -2 were employed to obtain the patterns in Fig. 27, the equivalent grating is a 4000 lines per inch grating. In Fig. 28 experimental and theoretical values are compared. The technique can also be applied to an embedded grating as shown in Fig. 29. The model is a rectangular plexiglass bar loaded in torsion.

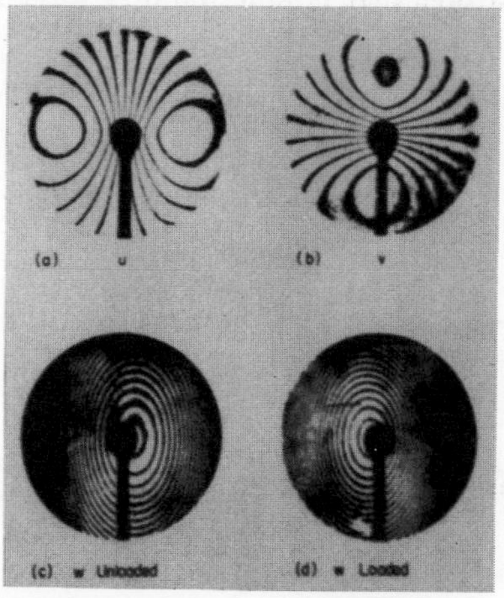

Fig. 27. Patterns corresponding to u, v and w displacements for circular plate.

Determination of the Deflection of Plates

Both in the case of diffuse illumination and collimated illumination the equations of the intensity distribution contain a term that depends on the gap existing between the model and reference grating, equation (51)

$$I(x) = I_o + I_1 \cos 2\pi \left[\overline{\psi}(x) + \frac{x\Delta z}{pz}\right] \qquad (130)$$

For the optical filtering set-up, equation (58)

$$I(x) = I_o + I_1 \cos 2\pi \left[\overline{\psi}(x) + \frac{t(\cos i - \cos r)}{\lambda}\right] \qquad (131)$$

In both cases, if the term $\overline{\psi}(x)$ is negligible with respect to the other term, as is the case of a plate, the observed patterns will correspond to the deflection of the plate. [29].

Projection of a Grating on a Matte Surface. Shadow Moiré. Reflection of a Grating on a Surface

The departure from flatness of a diffusely reflecting surface can be determined by means of the so called "shadow moiré" method, [30], [31], [32]. The surface is compared against a flat master with parallel lines. The master is placed near the surface and is illuminated with collimated light in a direction perpendicular to the rulings, but making an angle i with respect to the normal to the grating. The viewing direction is also perpendicular to the rulings but at an angle Φ with respect to the normal, Fig. 30.

The above described arrangement projects the grating on the deformed surface at an angle i and the distorted shape of the grating when viewed through

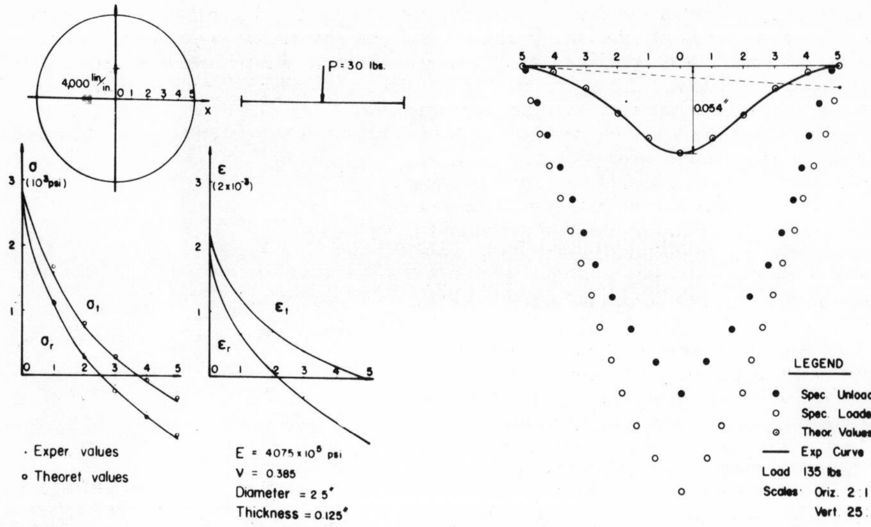

Fig. 28. Bending stresses, strains and deflections corresponding to circular plate; comparison of theoretical and experimental values.

the grating at an angle Φ, produces a moiré pattern that shows that departures of the surface from flatness.

From Fig. 30 it is easy to see that a point P is projected to P' on the surface, and when viewed telecentrically appears to be at P''. The displacements experienced by the point are

$$\Delta u_1 = w \operatorname{tg} i \tag{132}$$

$$\Delta u_2 = w \operatorname{tg} \Phi \tag{133}$$

The total displacement is

$$\Delta u = \Delta u_1 + \Delta u_2 = w (\operatorname{tg} i + \operatorname{tg} \Phi) \tag{134}$$

According to equation (24)

$$\Delta u = p\overline{\psi}(x) = w (\operatorname{tg} i + \operatorname{tg} \Phi) \tag{135}$$

$$\overline{\psi}(x) = \frac{w}{p} (\operatorname{tg} i + \operatorname{tg} \Phi) \tag{136}$$

a fringe will be observed each time $\overline{\psi}(x)$ is equal to an integer, then

$$w = \frac{np}{\operatorname{tg} i + \operatorname{tg} \Phi} \tag{137}$$

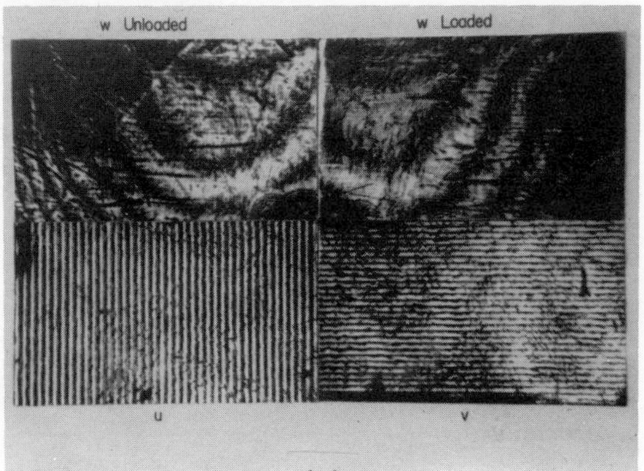

(a)

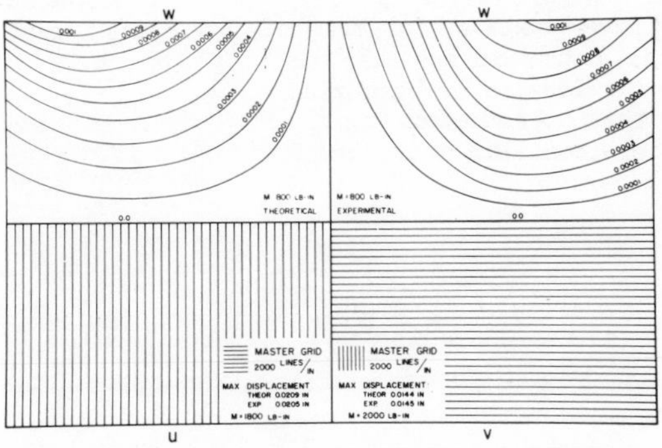

(b)

Fig. 29. Rectangular bar subjected to torsion. (a) Patterns of u, v and w displacements; (b) Comparison of theoretical and experimental values.

It is not necessary to have the master grating near the surface. One can project the grating by means of an optical projection system, and a second grating is added, to be utilized as viewing grating. However, this system has limitations concerning the pitch of the projected grating due to loss of contrast. Fig. 31 shows the "shadow" moiré pattern of a circular clamped grating loaded in the center. If laser light is utilized this phenomenon can be observed with very large ratios of the gap to the grating pitch.

The "shadow moiré" method can also be applied to curve surfaces. Reference gratings may be flat or curved [33], [34].

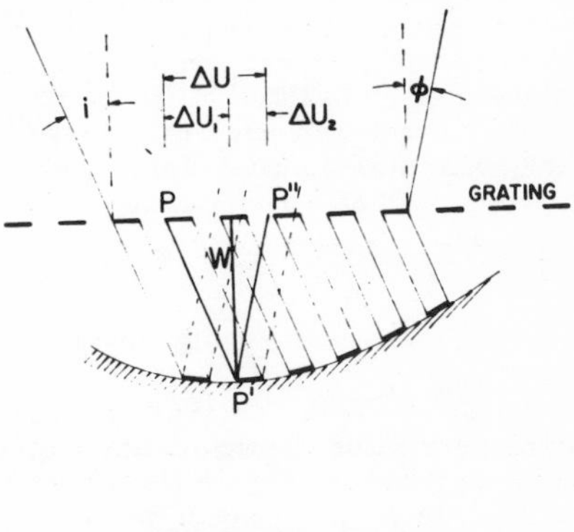

Fig. 30. Formation of "shadow" moiré

If we consider a plate with a mirror-like surface, a reference grating located in front of the plate will be reflected by the plate. A virtual image is produced, and the grating and its image produce moiré fringes that depend on the gap between the grating and the surface. The gap part of equation (130) applies, but the gap observed is twice the actual gap since the virtual image of the grating appears to be behind the mirror surface at the same distance than the grating is in front of the mirror [35]. If a collimating system similar to the one used to filter a single order is utilized, the gap part of equation (131) applies, but again the measured gap is twice the actual gap [36].

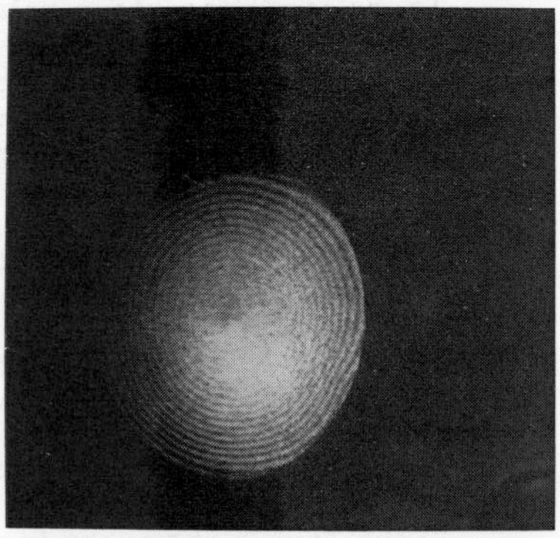

Fig. 31. Shadow moiré of a clamped circular plate loaded at its center.

A method to obtain the partial slopes of flexed plates was developed by Ligtenberg [37].

Fig. 32 shows a modification of the Ligtenberg method made by Rieder, [37]. This method provides a simple way of observing moiré patterns by reflection. From Fig. 31 we can see that the camera records in the undeformed position a point P of the grating. Assuming small deflections, after deformation the image experiences a displacement

$$u = 2d\theta \quad (138)$$

where d is the distance from the grating to the plate and θ is the change of angle between the initial and final positions from (24)

$$u = p\,\overline{\psi}(x) = 2d\theta \quad (139)$$

Fringes are observed each time that $\overline{\psi}(x)$ is an integer, then

$$\theta = \frac{np}{2d} \quad (140)$$

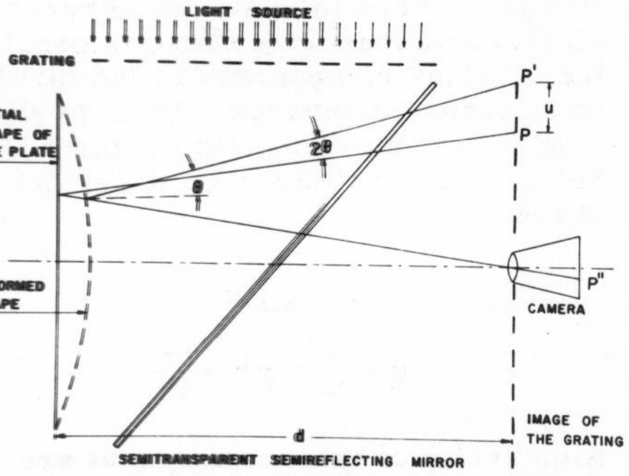

Fig. 32. Schematic representation of an optical set-up used in the Ligtenberg method for the measurement of relative slopes in flexed plates.

The measured angle is the inclination of the bent plate in the direction normal to the grating lines. Two moiré patterns are required to analyze the plate. In place of utilizing the superposition technique one can project a grating on the surface of the plate and a second grating can be introduced as a viewing grating.

The Ligtenberg method can also be applied to curve surfaces, [33], [39].

HOLOGRAPHY AND MOIRÉ

We can see now that the idea of utilizing gratings as carriers of displacement information has proven to be a very fruitful one. The displacements produce modulations on the phase of the carrier and the modulation function, or its rate of change can be detected by means of the moiré phenomenon. The carrier can be fixed on the surface to be analyzed. In such a case the in-plane and the out of plane displacements can be easily separated. The carrier can be optically projected on the surface, and if the surface is reflective or diffusive, displacements perpendicular to the plane of the grating can be found. If the surface is a reflecting surface, the slopes of the surface can also be determined.

There is a very close relationship between the described moiré techniques and the holographic technique recently introduced. A hologram is an interferogram of the object and the reference wavefronts on a plane surface (photographic plate surface), Fig. 33. We can consider an interferogram as the mapping of a wave-front by another wave-front. This mapping is given under the form of contour lines (interference fringes) corresponding to units of wave length. In holography this mapping is projected on the surface of the hologram. If we think of the equal phase lines representing the object wavefront and the reference wavefronts in the holographic plate, the hologram is the moiré produced by these two families of lines.

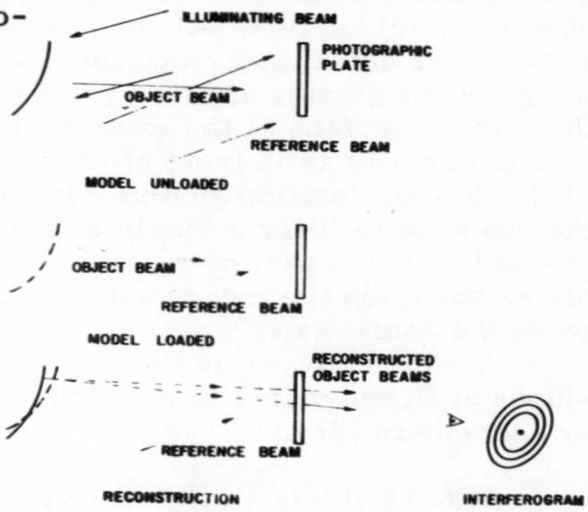

Fig. 33. Schematic representation of holographic interferometry by superposition.

In the double exposure technique two holograms are printed together and later reconstructed simultaneously. The reconstructed image is covered by fringes and these fringes represent the displacements of the points of the loaded model with respect to its unloaded or initial position. The obtained hologram depends on the direction of the beam that illuminates the object. The appearance of the hologram in the reconstruction process depends also on the direction of observation, since the reconstruction of both objects is three-dimensional, and therefore there is parallax between the two images. Consequently, the obtained components of the displacements depend on both illumination and observation directions. Fig. 34 shows two positions of a point and the corresponding displacement vector $\underset{\sim}{d}$ in the hologram. The observed difference of phase is

$$\Delta\varphi = \frac{2\pi}{\lambda} [AB + BC]$$
$$= \underset{\sim}{d} \cdot [\underset{\sim}{i} + \underset{\sim}{r}] \frac{2\pi}{\lambda} \qquad (141)$$

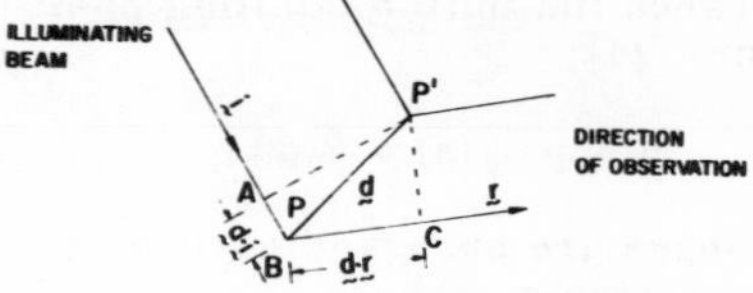

Fig. 34. Difference of optical paths corresponding to a point in holographic interferometry.

A difficulty of this technique at present is to obtain an easy and accurate way to solve equation (141). As we can see from equation (141) the displacements are measured in units of wave length.

With the present moiré technology let us say that we can utilize up to 10,000 l.p.i. gratings. The displacement corresponding to one fringe is then 0.0025 cm., and if we can measure 1/10 of a fringe we can reach a sensitivity of 0.00025 cm. If we compare the above quantity with the wave length of a helium-neon laser, 6328×10^{-8} cm., and since in double exposure holography each fringe is equivalent to a displacement of $\frac{\lambda}{4}$, we see that with moire we can reach $\frac{1}{16}$ of the sensitivity of holography.

Since holography in many cases is a too sensitive tool, moiré and holography can be looked upon as complementary techniques.

ACKNOWLEDGEMENT

The work done by the author in the moiré technique has been supported by sucessive grants of the National Science Foundation. The support of this institution is gratefully acknowledged.

The author is particularly grateful to Dr. M. Gauss of NSF for his understanding and continuous support of his work.

REFERENCES

1. Born, A. and Wolf, E., "Principle of Optics", Pergamon Press, (1959).

2. Sciammarella, C.A., "Basic Optical Law in the Interpretation of Moiré Patterns Applied to the Analysis of Strains, Part One", Exp. Mech., Vol. 5, No. 5, May 1965.

3. Sciammarella, C.A. and Sturgeon D., "Digital Filtering Techniques Applied to the Interpolation of Moiré Fringe Data", Exp. Mech., Vol. 7, No. 11, November 1967.

4. Sciammarella, C.A. and Durelli, A.J., "Moiré Fringes as a Means of Analyzing Strains", Proc. ASCE Vol. 87, No. EM 1, February 1961.

5. Sciammarella, C.A. and Chiang Fu-Pen, "Gap Effect on Moiré Patterns", Jnl. App. Mathematics and Physics (ZAMP) Vol. 19, Fasc. 2, 1968.

6. Sciammarella, C.A. and Sturgeon D., "Substantial Improvements in the Processing of Moiré Data by Optical and Digital Filtering". Proc. Third Int. Congress Exp. Stress Analysis, West Berlin, March 1966. VDI Berichte, No. 102, 1966.

7. Guild, J., "The Interference System of Crossed Diffraction Gratint s. Theory of Moiré Fringes." Oxford at the Clarendon Press, (1956).

8. Guild, J., "Diffraction Gratings as Measuring Scales", Oxford Univ. Press, London, 1960.

9. Dantu, P., "Utilisation des résaux pour l'étude des déformations". Laboratoire Central des Ponts et Chaussées, Paris, Publ. No. 57-6 (1957).

10. Parks, V.J. and Durelli, A.J., "Moiré Patterns of Partial Derivatives of Displacements Components," Jnl. Appl. Mech. 33, Series E (4), (1966).

11. Duncan, J.P. and Sabin, P.G., "An Experimental Method of Recording Curvature Contours in Flexed Elastic Plates", Exp. Mech. Vol. 5, No. 1 (1965).

12. Sciammarella, C.A. and Chang, T.Y., "Optical Differentiation of Displacement Patterns Using Shearing Interperometry by Wavefront Reconstruction", Exp. Mech., Vol. 11, No. 3 (1971).

13. Sciammarella, C.A., "Technique of Fringe Interpolation in Moiré Patterns". Second SESA Int. Congress Exp. Mech., Washington, D.C., 1966. Also Exp. Mech. Vol. 7, No. 11 (1967).

14. Sciammarella, C.A. and Doddington, C.W., "Effect of Photographic-film nonlinearities on the Processing of Moiré Fringe Data". Exp. Mech., Vol. 7, No. 9, (1967).

15. Sciammarella, C.A., "Automatic Data Retrieval and Data Processing Applied to Fringe Patterns Utilized in Experimental Stress Analysis". Proceedings Seminar-in-depth Pattern Recognition Studies, U.S.A. Army Materiel Command, Pattern Recognition Society, Society of Photo-optical Instrumentation Engineers. June 9-10, (1969).

16. Bossaert, W., Dechaene R., and Vinckier A., "Computation of Finite Strains from Moiré Displacements Patterns", Jnl. Strain Analysis, Vol. 3, No. 1, (1968).

17. Sciammarella, C.A. and Lurowist, N., "Multiplication and Interpolation of Moiré Fringe Orders by Purely Optical Techniques". Jnl. App. Mech. Vol. 34, Series E, No. 2, June 1967.

18. Sampson, R.C., and Campbell, D.M., "The Grid-Shift Technique for Moiré Analysis of Strain in Solid Propellant", Exp. Mech. Vol. 7, No. 11, (1967).

19. Chiang Fu-Pen, Parks, V.J. and Durelli, A.J., "Moiré Fringe Interpolation and Multiplication by Fringe Shifting", Exp. Mech., Vol. 8, No. 12 (1968).

20. Post, D., "Moiré Fringe Multiplication with a Nonsymmetrical Doubly Blazed Reference Grating", App. Optics Vol. 10, No. 4, (1971).

21. Sciammarella, C.A., "Elimination of the Effect of Lens Aberrations in Moiré Patterns produced by Optically Projecting the Master Grid on the Model Grid". Jnl. Appl. Mech., Vol. 34, Series E, No. 4, December 1967.

22. Sciammarella, C.A., "Moiré Fringe Multiplication by Means of Wave-Front Reconstruction Process". Exp. Mech., Vol. 9, April 1969.

23. Chiang, Fu-Pen, "Moiré Rosette Method for Strain Analysis", Report No. 145, State University, New York, Stony Brook, July 1969.

24. Dantu, P., "Application Rhéologiques De La Méthode Des Réseaux, Lab Central Des Ponts Et Chaussées, Pub. 61-5, (1961).

25. Dirury, M., "L'analyse des Contraintes par la méthode des réseaux optiques", Docaéro, No. 55, March 1959.

26. Sciammarella, C.A., "Theoretical and Experimental Study on Moiré Fringes", Illinois Institute of Technology, (June, 1960).

27. Chiang, Fu-Pen, "Method to Increase the Accuracy of the Moiré Method, Proc. ASCE, J. Eng. Mech. Div., Vol. 91, EMI (1965).

28. Sciammarella, C.A., Di Chirico, G. and Chang, T.Y., "Moiré-Holographic Technique for Three-Dimensional Strain Analysis"., Jnl. App. Mech., Vol. 37, Series E, No. 1, March 1970.

29. Chiang, Fu-Pen, "Deflection Measurement Using the Moiré Gap Effect", Report No. 152, State Univ., New York, Stony Brook (1970).

30. Weller, R. and Shepard, B.M., "Displacement Measurement by Mechanical Interferometry. Proc. Soc. Exp., Stress Anal. Vol. 6, No. 1, 1948.

31. Kaczer, J. and Kroupa, F., "The Determination of Strains by Mechanical Interference". Czechoslov. Jnl. Appl. Phys. Vol. 1, No. 2, 1952.

32. Theocaris, P.S., "Moiré Method in Plates", Proc. Int. Assoc. Shell Struc. Warsaw, North Holland, Amsterdam (1963).

33. Duncan, J.P., "The Optical Survey of Curved Surfaces", The University of British Columbia, (1966).

34. Theocaris, P.S., "Moiré Analysis of Cylindrical Surfaces", Proc. Third Int. Congress Exp. Stress Anal. West Berlin, March 1966, VDI Berichte, No. 102, 1966.

35. Ebeni, J., "Observation en incidence oblique des phénomenès de moiré pat réflection sur une plaque gauchie"; 1, Bull. Acad. Roy. Belg., 5 série, Vol. 50, No. 2 (1964).

36. Middleton, E., "A Reflection Technique for the Survey of the Reflection of Flat Plates", Exp. Mech., Vol. 8, No. 2 (1968).

37. Ligtenberg, F. K., "The Moiré Method: A New Experimental Method for the Determination of Moments in Small Slab Models", Proc. Soc. Exp. Stress Anal. Vol. 12, No. 2 (1954).

38. Rieder, G., "Krümmungsmessung an belasteten Platten nach dem Ligtenbergshem Moiré - Verfahren", Ver. Deut. Ing. Forseh. Ing. Wes. Vol. 31, No. 2, (1965).

39. Osgerby, C., "Application of the Moiré Method for use in the Cylindrical Surfaces", Exp. Mech. Vol. 7, No. 7, (1967).